BLUEPRINT

Maths
Key Stage 1
Copymasters

C000119420

Second edition

Wendy and David Clemson

Stanley Thornes (Publishers) Ltd

Do you receive BLUEPRINTS NEWS?

Blueprints is an expanding series of practical teacher's ideas books and photocopiable resources for use in primary schools. Books are available for separate infant and junior age ranges for every core and foundation subject, as well as for an ever widening range of other primary teaching needs. These include **Blueprints Primary English** books and **Blueprints Resource Banks. Blueprints** are carefully structured around the demands of the National Curriculum in England and Wales, but are used successfully by schools and teachers in Scotland, Northern Ireland and elsewhere.

Blueprints provide:
- *Total curriculum coverage*
- *Hundreds of practical ideas*
- *Books specifically for the age range you teach*
- *Flexible resources for the whole school or for individual teachers*
- *Excellent photocopiable sheets – ideal for assessment and children's work profiles*
- *Supreme value.*

Books may be bought by credit card over the telephone and information obtained on **(01242) 577944**. Alternatively, photocopy and return this **FREEPOST** form to receive **Blueprints News**, our regular update on all new and existing titles. You may also like to add the name of a friend who would be interested in being on the mailing list.

Please add my name to the **BLUEPRINTS NEWS** mailing list.

Mr/Mrs/Miss/Ms _____

Home address _____

_____ Postcode _____

School address _____

_____ Postcode _____

Please also send **BLUEPRINTS NEWS** to:

Mr/Mrs/Miss/Ms _____

Address _____

_____ Postcode _____

To: Marketing Services Dept., Stanley Thornes Ltd, FREEPOST (GR 782), Cheltenham, GL50 1BR

Text © Wendy and David Clemson 1995
Original line illustrations by Kim Blundell © ST(P) Ltd 1995

The right of Wendy and David Clemson to be identified as authors of this work has been asserted by them in accordance with the Copyright, Designs and Patents Act 1988.

The copyright holders authorise ONLY users of *Blueprints: Maths Key Stage 1 Copymasters* to make photocopies or stencil duplicates of the copymasters in this book for their own or their classes' immediate use within the teaching context. No other rights are granted without permission in writing from the publisher or under licence from the Copyright Licensing Agency Limited. Further details of such licences (for reprographic reproduction) may be obtained from the Copyright Licensing Agency Limited of 90 Tottenham Court Road, London W1P 9HE. Copy by any other means or for any other purpose is strictly prohibited without prior written consent from the copyright holders. Application for such permission should be addressed to the publishers.

Material from National Curriculum Orders is reproduced with the permission of the Controller of Her Majesty's Stationery Office.

First published in 1992 by:
Stanley Thornes (Publishers) Ltd
Ellenborough House
Wellington Street
CHELTENHAM GL50 1YW
England

Reprinted 1993 (twice), 1994

Second edition 1995

Reprinted 1995

A catalogue record for this book is available from the British Library.

ISBN 0–7487–2221–1

Typeset by Tech-Set, Gateshead, Tyne & Wear.
Printed and bound in Great Britain.

CONTENTS

Contents

INTRODUCTION

In this book there are 113 photocopiable worksheets. C1–C101 are linked specifically to activities in the *Teacher's Resource Book*. C102 is a teacher record sheet. R1–R11 are so called because they are resource copymasters and are intended for use again and again across all sections of the book. Where the photocopy sheets are referred to in the text of the *Teacher's Resource Book* there are some instructions on how to use them. They are referred to by number in the *Teacher's Resource Book* by this symbol:

When the children have completed these worksheets they can be added to workfiles or used as exemplar material in pupil profiles. You may also wish to use completed worksheets as a resource for your assessments. There is a tick list on copymaster C102, on which you can note the photocopy sheets the children have used.

Name _____

Conservation of 5

Colour and count

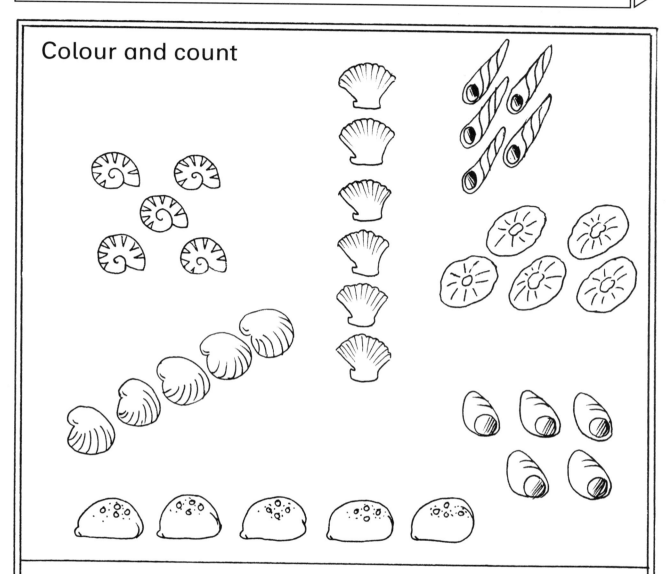

Draw more patterns of 5

Conservation of 2, 3, 5

Colour groups of 2 red, 3 blue and 5 green

Name _____

Ladybird race

Name _____

Cheese chase

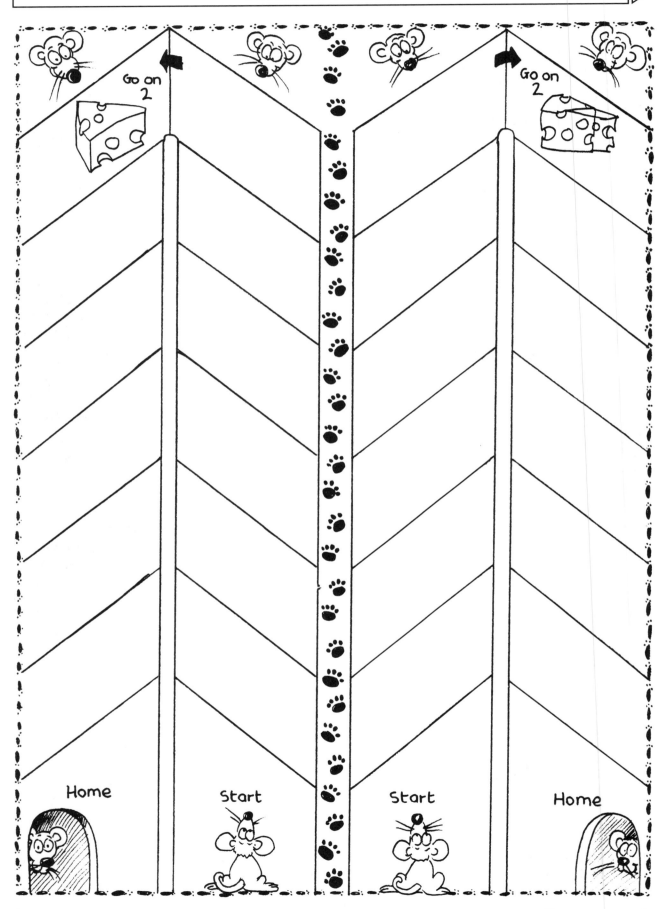

Copymaster 4

Home-time!

Name _____

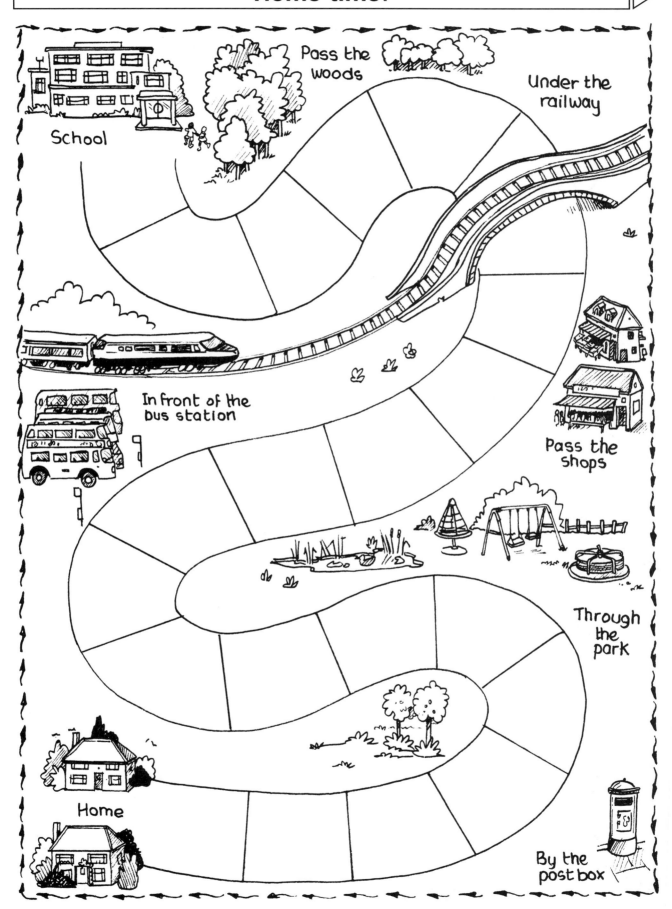

School

Pass the woods

Under the railway

In front of the bus station

Pass the shops

Through the park

Home

By the post box

Aliens

Name _____

Odds and evens

Write in – odd or even

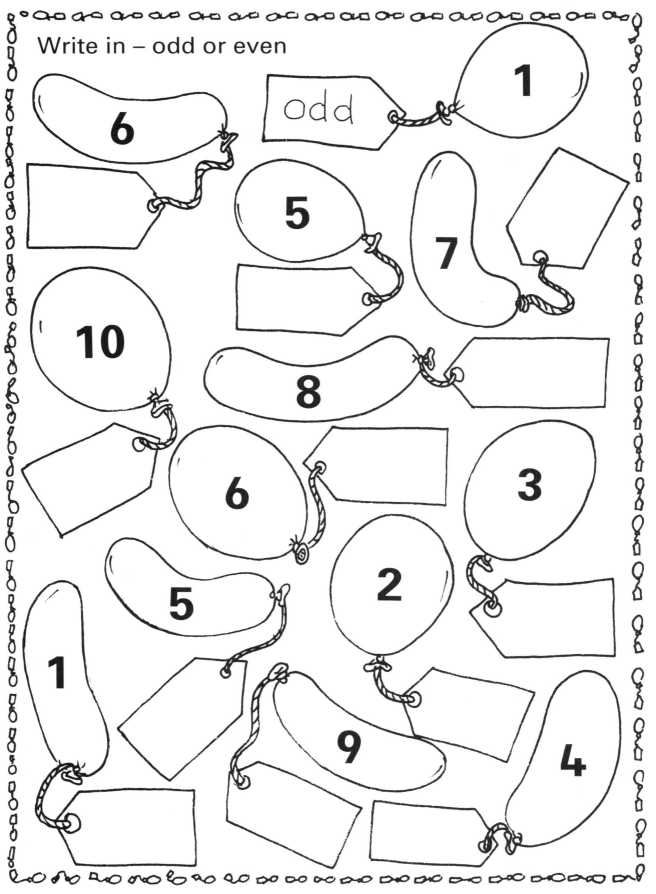

Name _____

Prize winning numbers

GRAND TOMBOLA

All the odd numbers win a prize!

Colour the numbers that win a prize

24 6 1 22 3
14 4 11 8
18 23
21 9 12 2
15 7
10 13 19
16 5 17 20 25

Numeral-set match

Match

1

2

3

4

5

6

Name _____

Counting and recording counts

How many?

Name _____

Counting and recording counts

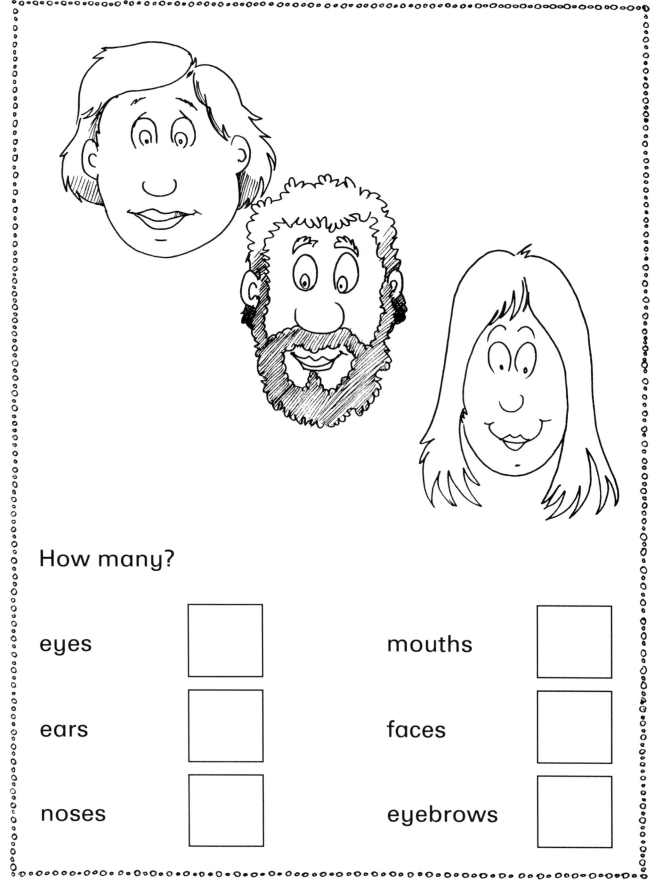

How many?

eyes ⬜   mouths ⬜

ears ⬜   faces ⬜

noses ⬜   eyebrows ⬜

Counting and recording counts

How many?

Name _____

Pairs

How many pairs?

	pair of eyes
	pair of ears
	pair of lips
	pair of hands
	pair of arms
	pair of legs
	pair of feet
	pair of socks
	pair of trainers

Ordinal numbers

Who will win the race?

Write 1st 2nd 3rd by the cars

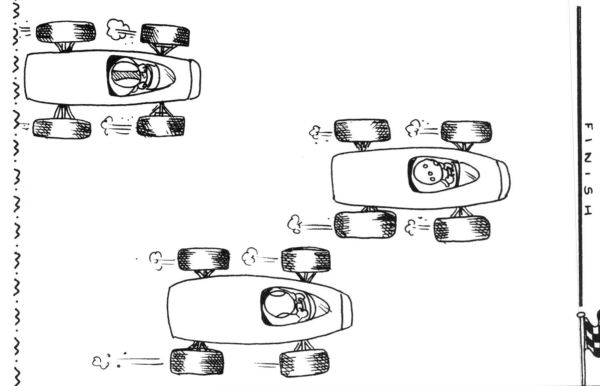

Match

second   fourth   third   first

3rd   1st   4th   2nd

Name _____

Tens and units

Set these out as tens and units

14   27   74   32   46

Look for the pattern

15   25   35   45   55

Which is the biggest number
in these?

19   11   39   91   48

These are easy if you know the pattern

10   20   30   40   50

Thousands, hundreds, tens and units

Set these out as hundreds, tens and units

100   105   150   151   501

Try this for size! You need a thousands column

4321

Do these in order of size. Start with the smallest

122   5011   36   95   14

These numbers make a pattern

250   500   750   1000   1250

Big numbers in words

Write these in numerals

How do you write these?

TWENTY-NINE

SIXTY-SEVEN

ONE HUNDRED AND EIGHTEEN

FIFTY-TWO

ONE HUNDRED AND SEVENTY

I enjoyed those. Now for some more.

TWO THOUSAND AND NINETY-TWO

EIGHT THOUSAND AND ELEVEN

EIGHTY-EIGHT

FOUR THOUSAND AND TWENTY-THREE

ONE HUNDRED AND ONE

Name _____

Halves

Ring a half ($\frac{1}{2}$) of these

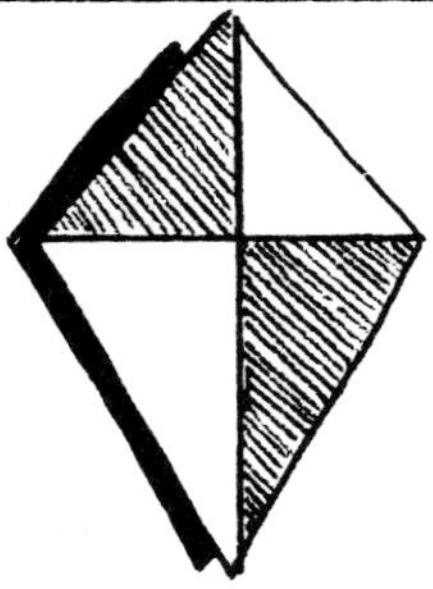

kite

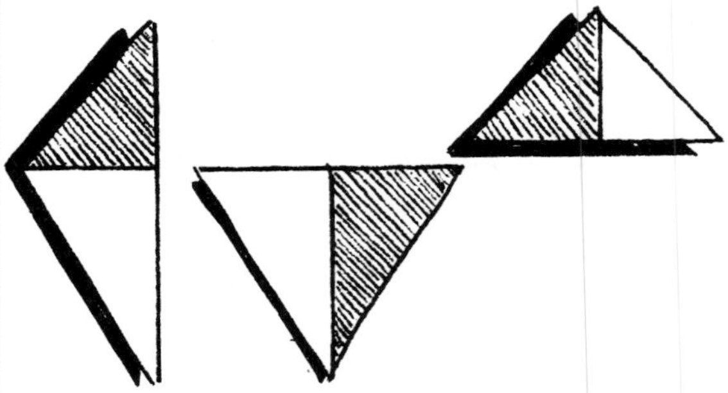

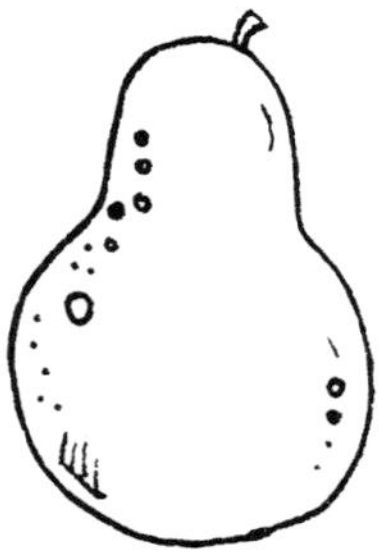

pear

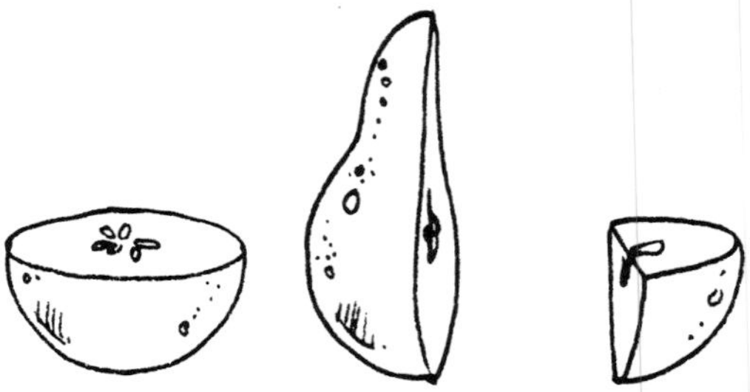

lolly

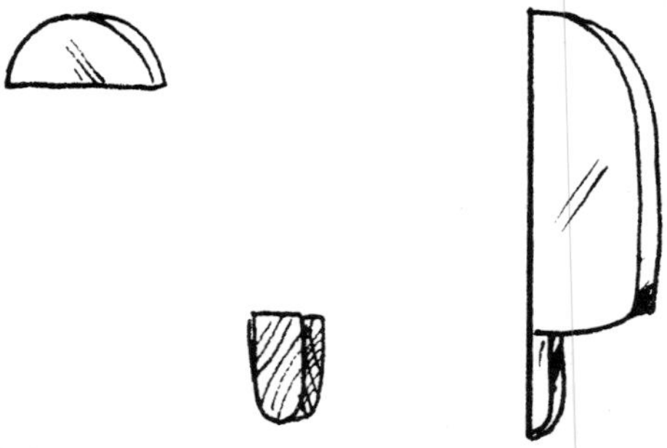

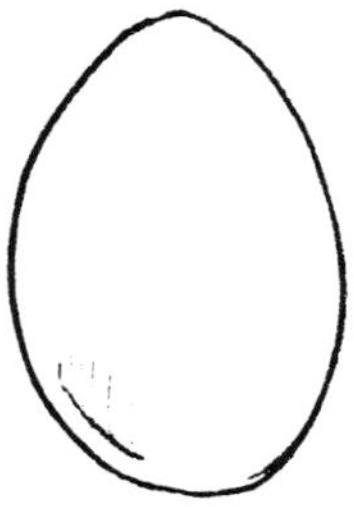

egg

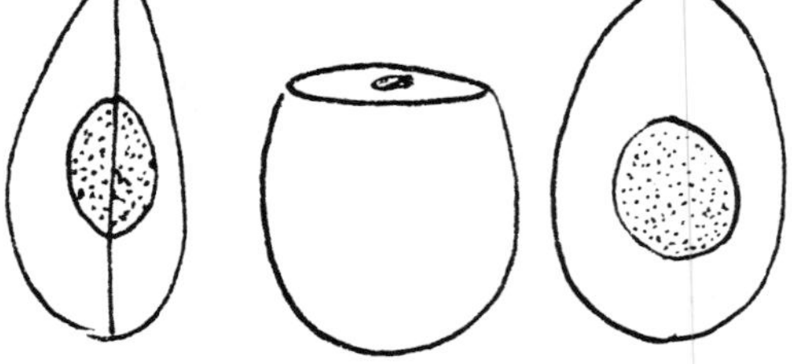

piece of paper

Name _____

Quarters

Ring a quarter ($\frac{1}{4}$) of these

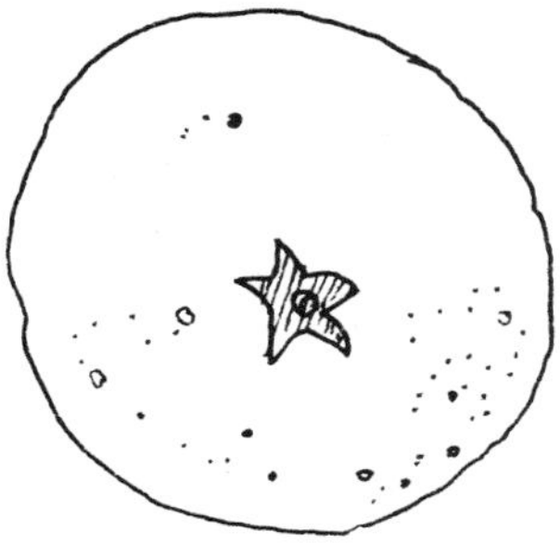

orange

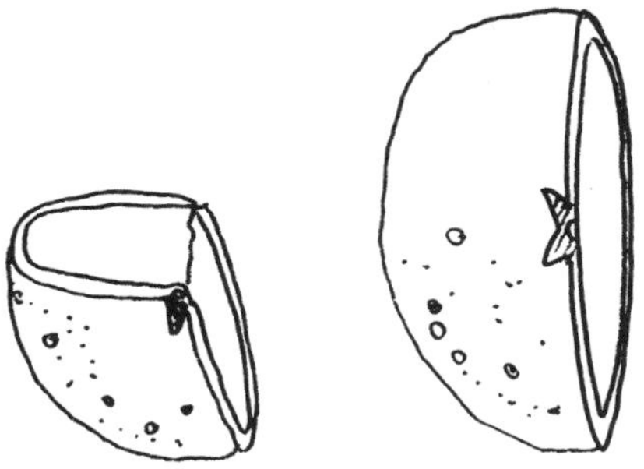

cheese sandwich

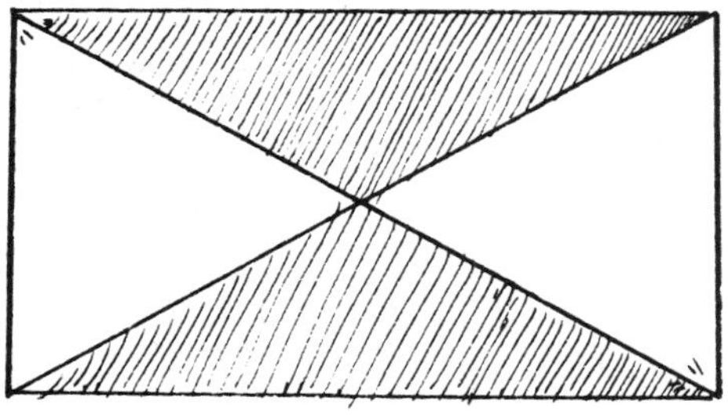

flag

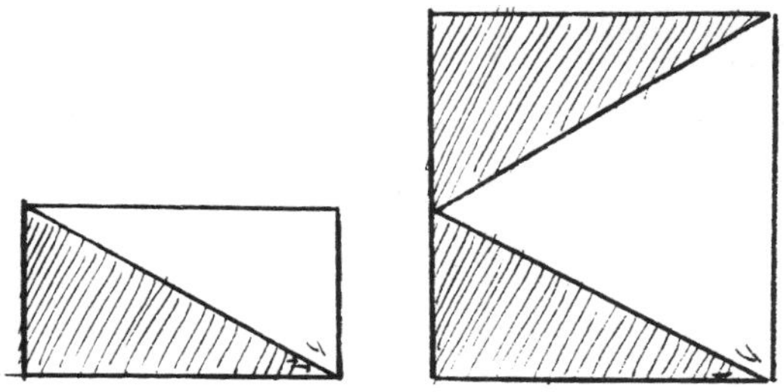

cherry cake

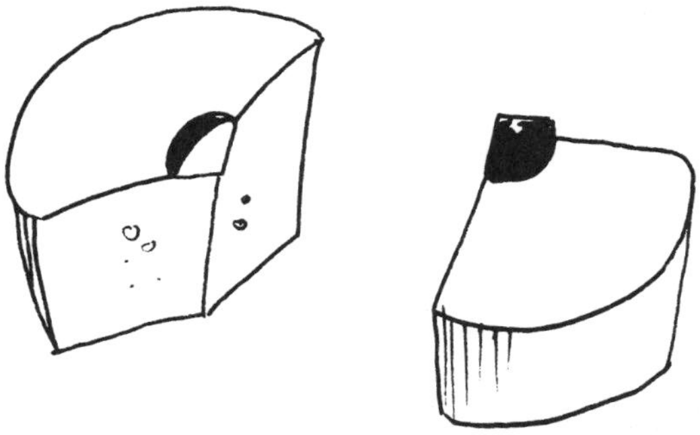

Name _____

Tickets, bills and receipts

A supermarket receipt

	£
Catfood	0.29
Catfood	0.26
Red apples	1.98
Pk. sausages	1.09
Peas	0.79
Fresh chicken	4.12
New potatoes	0.66
Mild cheddar	0.65
Rasp. yogurt	1.03
Balance due	9.87
Cash	10.00
Change	0.13

A bus ticket

CLASS	CHILD	ADULT
ORD	NIL	ONE 1
	0	1

STD	BUS	ROUTE	FOR
1	157	175 B	1

START   GET

PRICE ..   0·60p

A rail ticket

CLASS	TICKET TYPE	ADULT	CHILD
STD	CHEAP BREAK	ONE	NIL OUT

DATE   NUMBER
11 MAY 92   402123 6·7311

FROM
MILTON KEYNES   VALID
OUT 1D KING   PRICE
£11·80 m

TO
HARROW WEALDSTONE   ROUTE
1325

≥ BRITISH RAIL

£5.05

Bar code

95p

Price tags

46

17:14

1·32

55p

74·15

Jones the Papers
6, High Street, Newtown
Longshire LN4 PP1

DELIVERY ADDRESS
Williams
72 Lower Lane
Newton Longshire

INVOICE NUMBER 1073

	£	
Newspapers 14th July to 25th August	25	95
Delivery charge	1	00
Total Due	26	95

Shopping list

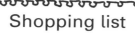

Bill

Money problems

Robin has 52p. She buys

She has ☐ left.

How much did he spend altogether?

She spends the rest.

Joan has 50p.

She gives 15p to her sister.

She puts 15p in her piggy bank.

How much does she spend?

Cherry cake 14p   Sausage roll 23p   Apple turnover 19p

You have 60p to spend. You may buy more than one of each. Draw what you could have and write how much change you would get.

change ☐   change ☐   change ☐

Copymaster 21

Name _____

Shopping – track

Name _____

Shopping lists

Toys. Buy these in the toy shop or post office.

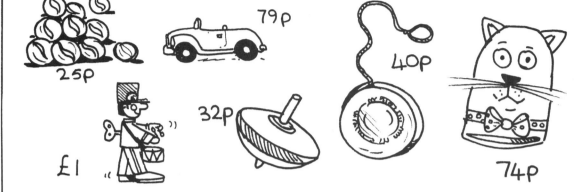

25p   79p   40p   74p
£1   32p

Stationery. Buy these in the toy shop or post office.

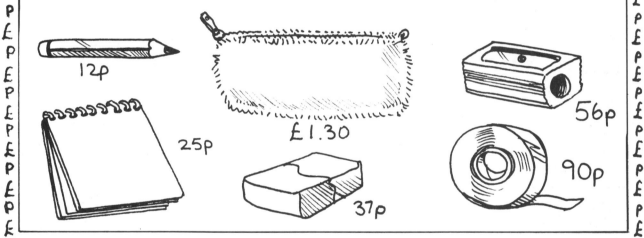

12p   £1.30   56p
25p   37p   90p

Sweets. Buy these in the sweet shop or post office.

55p
15p   25p   39p   11p   £2.05

Name _____

Examples with some negative numbers

20 + 0 = ☐   9 + 4 = ☐   11 − 15 = ☐

17 − 7 = ☐   5 − 8 = ☐

8 − 9 = ☐

Six done! Three have negative answers.

4 − 5 = ☐   3 + 6 = ☐

10 − 5 = ☐   6 − 7 = ☐

12 + 6 = ☐

Another five done. How many of these have negative answers?

2 + 11 = ☐   ☐ = 9 + 9

13 + 5 = ☐   ☐ = 9 − 11

7 − 10 = ☐   ☐ = 8 − 2

Name _____

Patterns around you

Can you find these patterns in things around you?

Where? Draw or write.

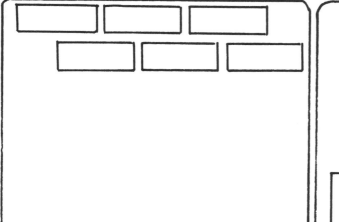

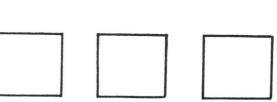

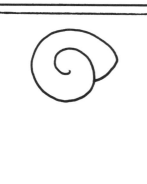

121212

┼┼┼

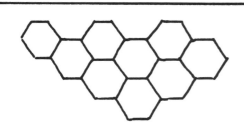

/\\/\\/\\

Name _____

Number patterns

Continue the patterns. Then play and check.

1 2 3 1 2 3 _____

4 6 4 6 4 6 _____

3 5 1 3 5 1 _____

7 2 7 2 7 2 _____

5 1 5 1 _____

6 2 6 2 _____

2 3 2 3 _____

7 3 7 3 1 7 3 7 3 1 _____

5 4 3 8 5 4 3 8 _____

1 2 1 3 1 2 1 3 _____

1 2 3 4 5 1 2 3 4 5 _____

Number bonds

Make 5	Make 2	Make 3	Make 4
0 + 5	0 + 2	0 + 3	0 + 4
1 +	1 +	1 +	1 +
2 +	2 +	2 +	2 +
3 +		3 +	3 +
4 +	**Make 5**		4 +
5 +	10 −	**Make 7**	
	9 −	10 −	**Make 6**
Make 10	8 −	9 −	10 −
0 + 10	7 −	8 −	9 −
1 +	6 −	7 −	8 −
2 +	5 −		7 −
3 +		**Make 7**	6 −
4 +	**Make 5**	− 0	
5 +	− 0	− 1	**Make 6**
6 +	− 1	− 2	− 0
7 +	− 2	− 3	− 1
8 +	− 3		− 2
9 +	− 4		− 3
10 +	− 5		− 4

Name _____

Number arrays

Continue the patterns

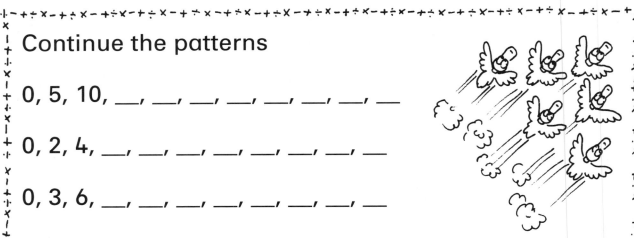

0, 5, 10, __, __, __, __, __, __, __, __

0, 2, 4, __, __, __, __, __, __, __, __

0, 3, 6, __, __, __, __, __, __, __

0, 10, 20, __, __, __, __, __, __, __, __

2 + 10 = 12	90 − 10 = 80
12 + 10 =	80 − 10 =
22 + 10 =	70 − 10 =
32 + 10 =	60 − 10 =

What is missing?

30, 35, 40, __, __, 55, __, __, __

24, 26, __, __, __, 34, 36, __, __

42, 45, 48, __, __, __, __

100, 90, __, __, __, __, __, __

27, 24, 21, __, __, __, __, __

20, 18, 16, __, __, __, __, __, __

Name _____

Leap frog

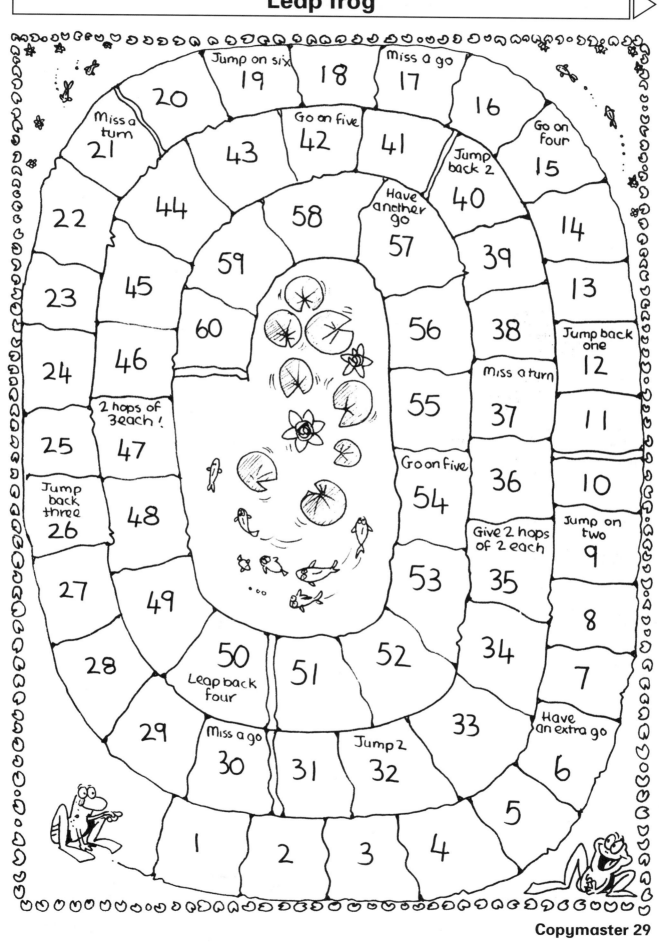

Planes and parachutes

Finish			Down you go						
100	99	98	97	96	95	94	93	92	91
81	82	83	84	85	86	87	88	89	90
80	79	78	Down you go 77	76	75	74	73 Take off	72	71
61	62	63	64	65	66	Down you go 67	68	69	70
60 Take off	59	58	57	56	55	54	53	52	51
41	42	43	44	45	46	47 Take off	Down you go 48	49	50
40	39	38	37	36	35	34	33	32	31
21	22	23	24	25	26	27	28 Take off	29	Down you go 30
20	19 Take off	18	17	16	15	14	13	12	11
1 Start	2	3 Take off	4	5 Take off	6	7	8	9	10

Copymaster 30

Name _____

Take away strips

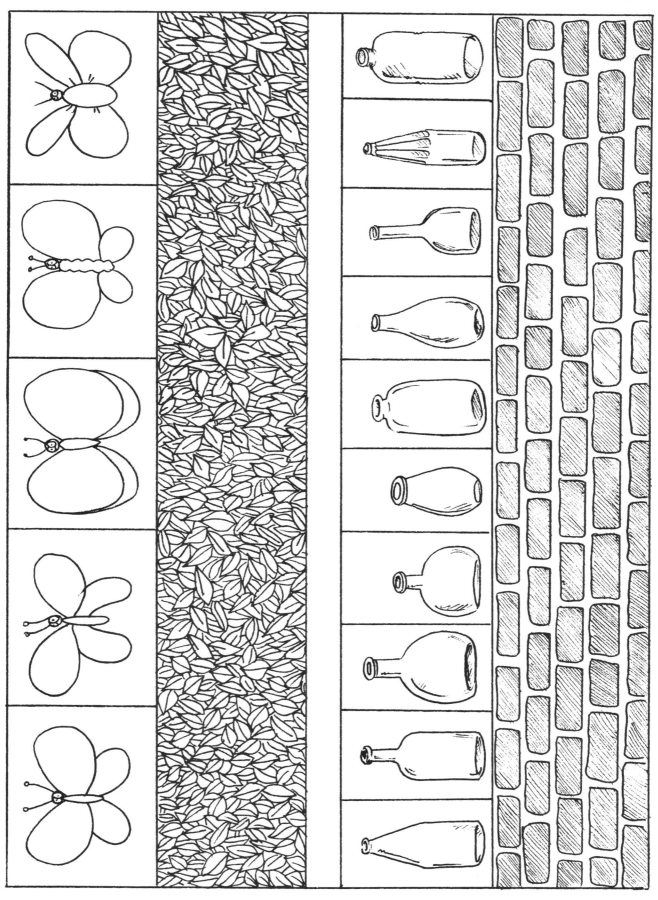

Name _____

Make five

1		2		3		5	
1		2		2		2	
	1		2		3		3
	1		1		1		5
	1		1		1		5
	3		1		1		1
	2		3		1		1
	1		1		2		4
	4		1		1		1

Name _____

Make ten

9	1	8	2
7	3	6	4
5	5	4	6
5	5	3	7
2	8	9	1
2	3	5	4
1	5	6	3
1	8	1	1
7	2	1	9

Subtraction bonds to 20

20 − 10	20 − 5	20 − 0	20 − 20

Join up like this

20   10   0   15

20 − 8	20 − 6	20 − 4	20 − 2

18   14   16   12

20 − 18	20 − 16	20 − 14	20 − 12

4   2   6   8

20 − 19	20 − 17	20 − 15	20 − 13

5   1   3   7

20 − 11	20 − 9	20 − 7	20 − 3

11   9   17   13

Name _____

Bingo

Base cards

17 − 11	10 − 5	4 + 2
7 + 8	13 − 3	10 + 10

5 − 5	18 − 7	9 + 5
7 − 3	14 + 2	12 + 8

19 − 7	15 − 5	8 + 2
5 − 0	16 + 3	8 + 9

20 − 10	9 − 6	17 − 9
4 + 12	8 − 5	10 − 10

Numerals

6	5	6	0	11	14
15	10	20	4	16	20
12	10	10	10	3	8
5	19	17	16	3	0

Missing numbers

0, 2, _____, 6, 8, _____, _____, 14, 16, _____, 20

0, 3, 6, _____, _____, 15, 18, 21, _____, _____, _____

0, 4, _____, 12, _____, 20, _____, 28, _____, 36, _____

0, 5, 10, _____, _____, _____, 30, 35, 40, _____, _____

0, 6, _____, 18, _____, 30, _____, 42, 54, 60

0, 7, 14, _____, _____, 35, _____, _____, 56, _____, 70

0, 8, _____, _____, 32, 40, _____, _____, 64, 72, _____

0, 9, _____, 27, 36, _____, _____, 63, 72, _____, 90

0, 10, _____, _____, _____, 50, 60, 70, _____, _____, _____

What's next in the pattern?

9, 12, 15, _____   35, 42, _____   60, 70, _____

10, 12, _____   20, 25, _____   8, 16, _____

Name _____

Zap!

Name _____

Multiply cards for Zap

1×2	2×2	3×2	4×2
5×2	6×2	7×2	8×2
9×2	10×2	1×3	3×3
4×3	5×3	6×3	7×3
8×3	9×3	10×3	1×5
4×5	5×5	6×5	7×5
8×5	9×5	10×5	1×10
4×10	6×10	7×10	8×10
9×10	10×10		

Copymaster 38

Name _____

Multiplication ladders

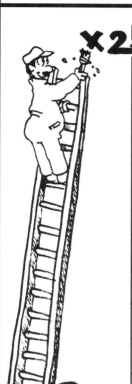

×2

0 × 2 = 0	
1 × 2 =	
2 × 2 =	
3 × 2 =	
4 × 2 =	
5 × 2 =	
6 × 2 =	
7 × 2 =	
8 × 2 =	
9 × 2 =	
10 × 2 =	

×3

0 × 3 = 0	
1 × 3 =	
2 × 3 =	
3 × 3 =	
4 × 3 =	
5 × 3 =	
6 × 3 =	
7 × 3 =	
8 × 3 =	
9 × 3 =	
10 × 3 =	

×5

0 × 5 = 0	
1 × 5 =	
2 × 5 =	
3 × 5 =	
4 × 5 =	
5 × 5 =	
6 × 5 =	
7 × 5 =	
8 × 5 =	
9 × 5 =	
10 × 5 =	

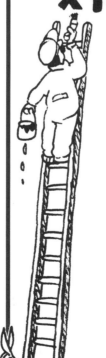

×10

0 × 10 = 0	
1 × 10 =	
2 × 10 =	
3 × 10 =	
4 × 10 =	
5 × 10 =	
6 × 10 =	
7 × 10 =	
8 × 10 =	
9 × 10 =	
10 × 10 =	

Picture sharing

Ann   Roberta   Liam

Lollipops. How many each? ☐

Ed   Fred

Honey pots. How many each? ☐

Worms. How many each? ☐

Cherries. How many each? ☐

Name _____

Division puzzles

20 bones

→ 2 dogs [ ] each

→ 4 dogs [ ] each

→ 5 dogs [ ] each

→ 10 dogs [ ] each

21p

→ 3 boys [ ] p each

→ 7 girls [ ] p each

30 people

→ 2 minibuses [ ] in each

→ 3 minibuses [ ] in each

→ 5 minibuses [ ] in each

→ 6 minibuses [ ] in each

→ 10 minibuses [ ] in each

Name _____

Divide cards for Zap

2 ÷ 4	4 ÷ 2	6 ÷ 2	8 ÷ 2
10 ÷ 2	12 ÷ 2	14 ÷ 2	16 ÷ 2
18 ÷ 2	20 ÷ 2	3 ÷ 3	6 ÷ 3
9 ÷ 3	12 ÷ 3	15 ÷ 3	18 ÷ 3
21 ÷ 3	24 ÷ 3	27 ÷ 3	30 ÷ 3
5 ÷ 5	10 ÷ 5	15 ÷ 5	20 ÷ 5
25 ÷ 5	30 ÷ 5	35 ÷ 5	40 ÷ 5
45 ÷ 5	50 ÷ 5	10 ÷ 10	50 ÷ 10
100 ÷ 10			

Copymaster 42

Name _____

Calculator checks

Check these using a calculator

Give a tick for correct answers
Cross out wrong answers
Write in the correct answer

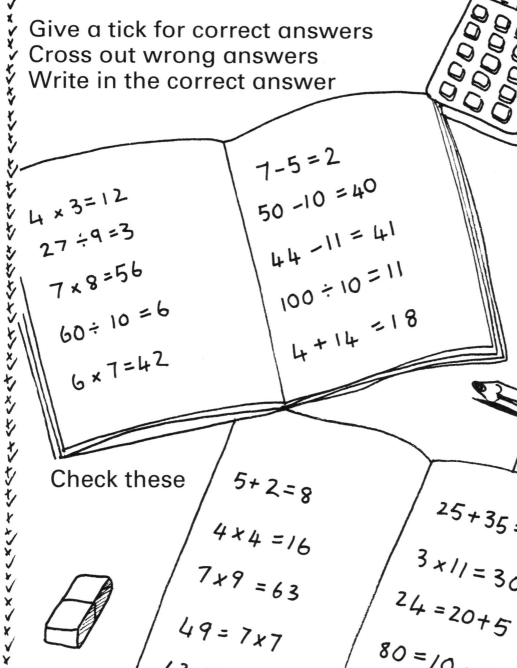

$4 \times 3 = 12$

$27 \div 9 = 3$

$7 \times 8 = 56$

$60 \div 10 = 6$

$6 \times 7 = 42$

$7 - 5 = 2$

$50 - 10 = 40$

$44 - 11 = 41$

$100 \div 10 = 11$

$4 + 14 = 18$

Check these

$5 + 2 = 8$

$4 \times 4 = 16$

$7 \times 9 = 63$

$49 = 7 \times 7$

$63 = 9 \times 8$

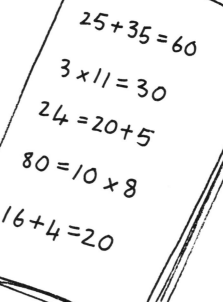

$25 + 35 = 60$

$3 \times 11 = 30$

$24 = 20 + 5$

$80 = 10 \times 8$

$16 + 4 = 20$

Name _____

Missing number mysteries

Find the missing numbers

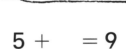

$5 +$ $= 8$

$7 +$ $= 10$

$4 +$ $= 6$

   $+ 4 = 8$

   $+ 1 = 3$

$3 -$ $= 2$

$7 -$ $= 6$

$2 -$ $= 1$

   $- 5 = 5$

   $- 7 = 1$

$5 +$ $= 9$

$2 +$ $= 4$

$3 +$ $= 9$

   $+ 5 = 6$

   $+ 2 = 7$

$8 -$ $= 5$

$9 -$ $= 7$

   $- 4 = 3$

   $- 2 = 8$

   $- 1 = 3$

Copymaster 44

Name _____

An add 3 robot

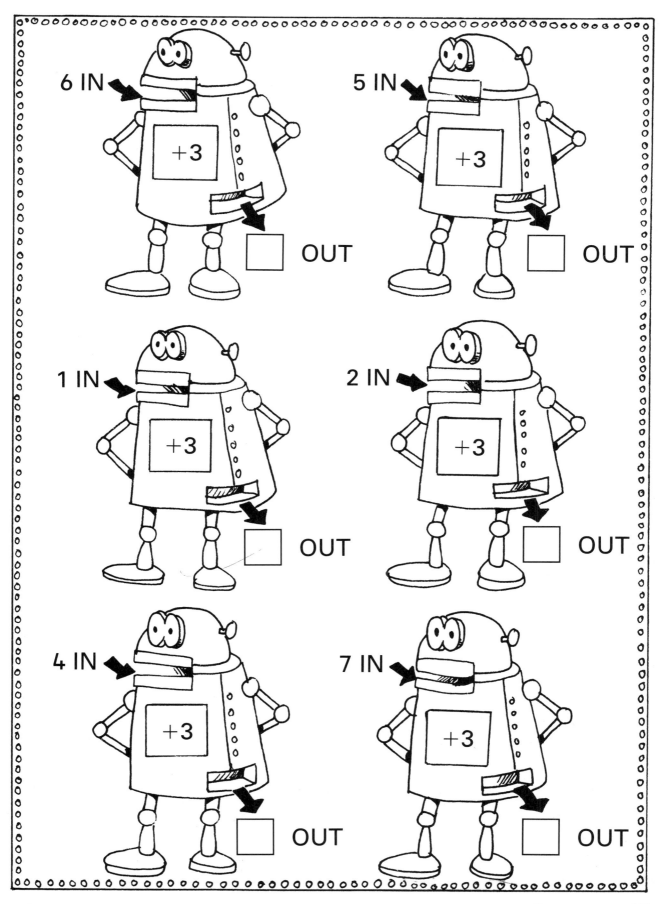

6 IN   +3   ☐ OUT

5 IN   +3   ☐ OUT

1 IN   +3   ☐ OUT

2 IN   +3   ☐ OUT

4 IN   +3   ☐ OUT

7 IN   +3   ☐ OUT

Name _____

A take away 2 machine

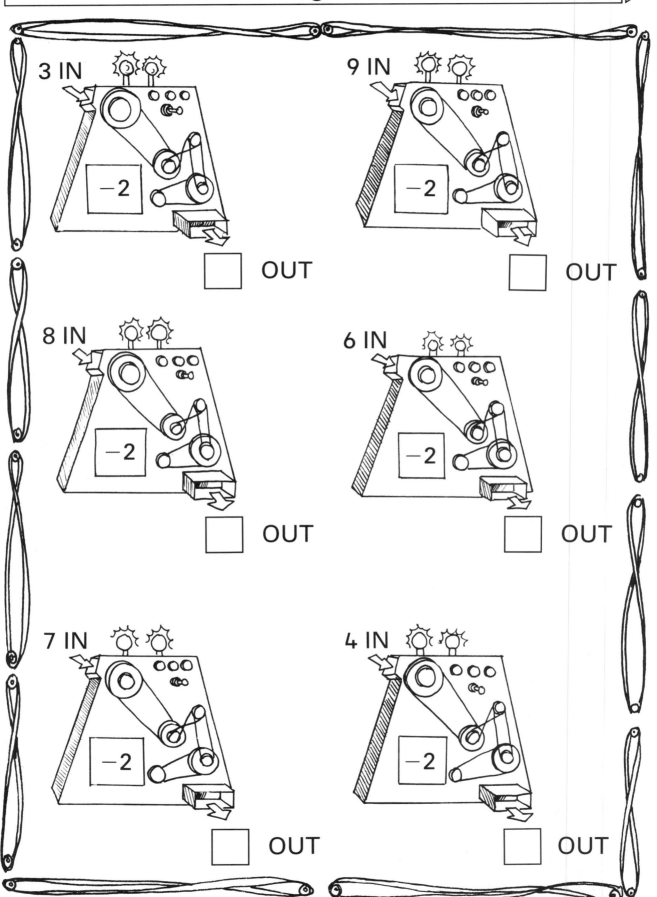

3 IN
-2

☐ OUT

9 IN
-2

☐ OUT

8 IN
-2

☐ OUT

6 IN
-2

☐ OUT

7 IN
-2

☐ OUT

4 IN
-2

☐ OUT

Computation trail

Start

Finish

5

Down the well +2

Through the tunnel −5

Over the bridge

+4

+8

Across the river

Up the tower +5

Into the caves −1

−3

Through the swamp

On the train −7

+6

Up the mountain −4

Over the forest

Add and subtract

10 − 3 →

7 − 1 →

5 − 2 →

8 − 4 →

9 − 5 →

2 − 1 →

How many did you do in your head?

I am a good adder!

4 + 2 →

4 + 6 →

7 − 3 →

7 + 3 →

5 + 5 →

10 − 5 →

9 − 6 →

What is missing?

7 − ☐ → 4

4 + ☐ → 8

6 + ☐ → 10

☐ + 2 → 5

☐ + 5 → 7

☐ + 3 → 9

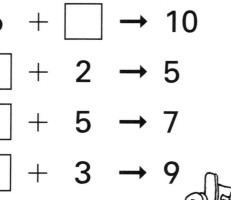

Put in the sign
+ or −?

5   5 → 10

6   2 → 4

7   2 → 9

3   2 → 5

6 → 3   3

5 → 8   3

4 → 2   2

Equivalence

Join those of equal value

Change

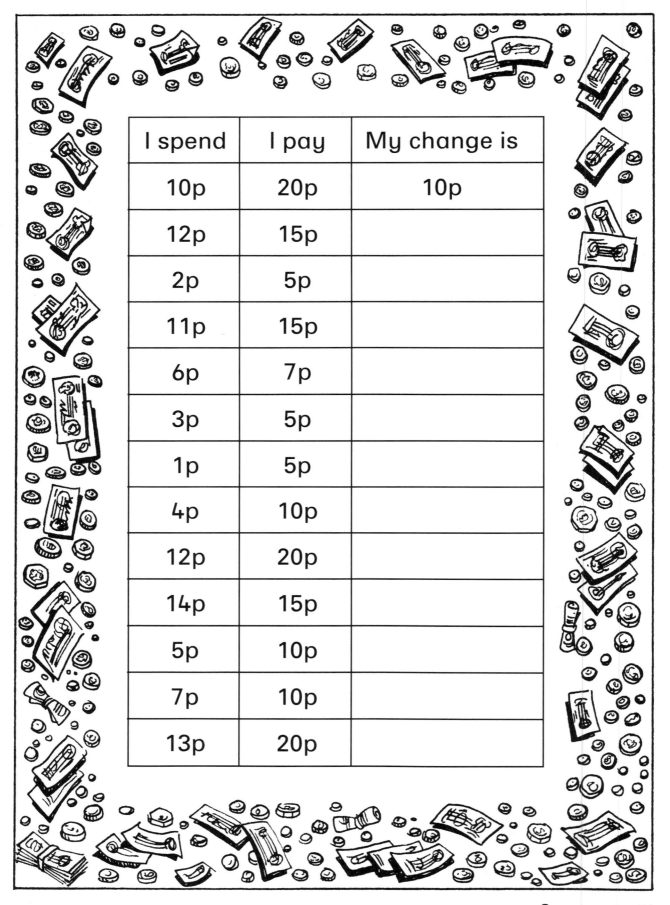

I spend	I pay	My change is
10p	20p	10p
12p	15p	
2p	5p	
11p	15p	
6p	7p	
3p	5p	
1p	5p	
4p	10p	
12p	20p	
14p	15p	
5p	10p	
7p	10p	
13p	20p	

An add 5 rocket

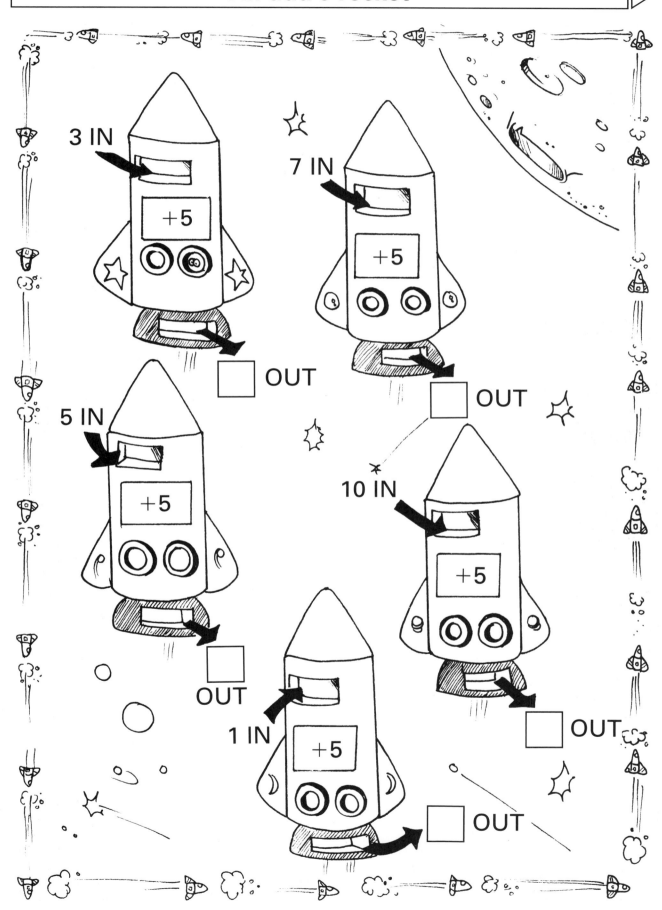

3 IN +5 ☐ OUT

7 IN +5 ☐ OUT

5 IN +5 ☐ OUT

10 IN +5 ☐ OUT

1 IN +5 ☐ OUT

Name _____

A take away 7 machine

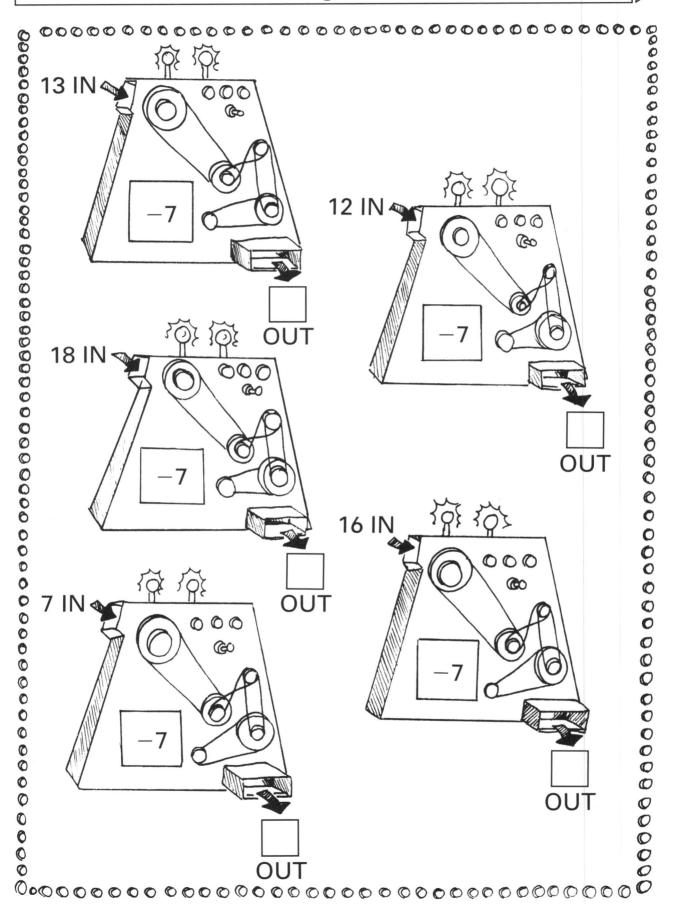

13 IN

−7

12 IN

−7

OUT

18 IN

−7

16 IN

OUT

7 IN

−7

−7

OUT

OUT

Name _____

Star wars machines

Follow the trail

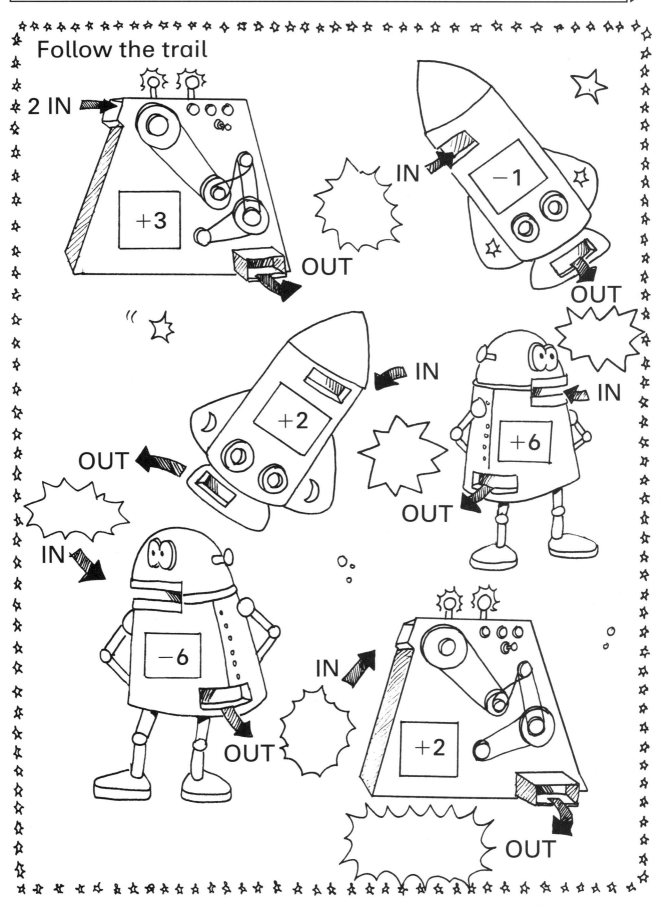

2 IN +3 OUT

IN −1 OUT

IN +2 OUT

IN +6 OUT

IN −6 OUT

IN +2 OUT

Name _____

Mystery machines

What do these machines do?

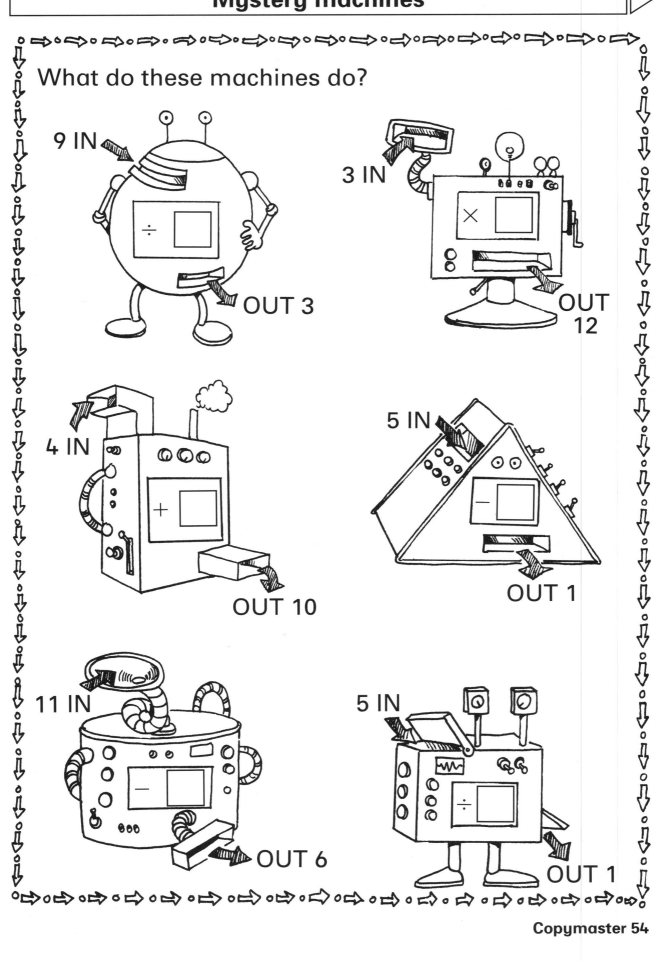

9 IN

OUT 3

3 IN

OUT 12

4 IN

OUT 10

5 IN

OUT 1

11 IN

OUT 6

5 IN

OUT 1

Choose how to compute ▷

The problem	Is it + − × or ÷?	How to do it
5 apples come off a tree and then 10 more. How many apples fall?		
Cake comes in packs of 8 slices. How many slices in 5 packs?		
Paints come in packs like this. BLUE PINK WHITE GREEN BLACK RED ORANGE If all the red and black is used how many pots are left?		
2 pizzas. Each in 6 pieces. How many people can have 3 slices each?		

Choose how to compute

The problem	Is it + − × or ÷?	How to do it
56 children are absent from a school with 203 pupils. How many are at school?		
How many toys in the lucky dip if 78 children can have 2 goes each?		
There are 11 people in a cricket team. How many teams can be made from 60 people?		
If 2 appears in half of all phone numbers, how many of 5438 phone numbers will have a 2 in them?		
Here are the numbers of people who go to the zoo each day. How many in total? 74 39 41 89		
An insect has 6 legs. How many legs on 60 insects?		

Tens and units: addition

Work out
the sums
in this space

		Answers
13 + 21		
25 + 62		
44 + 37		
90 + 9		
14 + 73		

Tens and units: subtraction

Show what you do
to get the answers

64 − 13		Answers
75 − 22		
38 − 15		
99 − 41		
50 − 25		

Add and subtract with approximation steps

Work out rough answers
to these

41 + 31	
69 + 22	
78 − 32	
51 + 39	
29 + 48	
61 − 20	

Now use your calculator to check.

Write your calculator answers here.

Mapping

Give each drink a straw

☐ drinks

☐ straws

Give each stick a toffee apple

☐ sticks

☐ toffee apples

Give each woman a mouth

☐ women

☐ mouths

Give each kite a string

☐ kites

☐ strings

Complex mapping

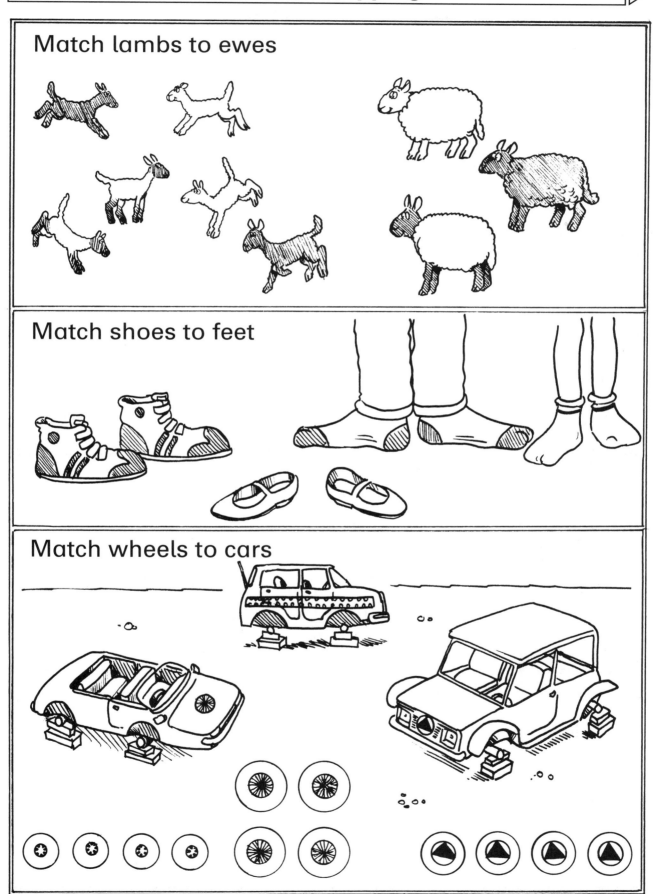

Match lambs to ewes

Match shoes to feet

Match wheels to cars

Weather frequency table

Weather ... a 20 day study

Key

| sunny day | cloudy day | rainy day |

	| | | |
	| | | | | | | | | |
	| | | | | |

Name _____

Frequency data collection

Key

What you are looking for

How many times it happens

Customer frequency table

Day of week	Number of customers between 9 o'clock and 10 o'clock		
	TV	Flowers	Fruit
Monday	|	|||	||
Tuesday	||	||||	||||
Wednesday	|||	||||	||||||
Thursday	|	||	||||||
Friday	|||||	|||||||||	|||||||||||
Saturday	||||	|||||||||	|||||||||

Name _____

Graph axes and grid

Problem cards for block graphs or bar charts

Find out what your classmates' favourite meals are

Find out your classmates' shoe sizes

What pets do your classmates have?

Find out your classmates' favourite colours

Shopping list and index

Where would you buy these things?

Shopping List
Tea
Cornflakes
Eggs
Cat food
Kitchen Roll
Biscuits

How many items are on the list? ☐

What comes after 'eggs'? _____

What is the first item? _____

What is the last item? _____

Index to _____

Write in the title of your book

What is the first word in the index? _____

What is the first word under these letters?

M _____   K _____

E _____   Y _____

S _____   D _____

What is the last word in the index? _____

What letters of the alphabet have
no entries in the index? _____

Copymaster 67

Pictograms

How many girls in a class?

Key ♀ 6 girls

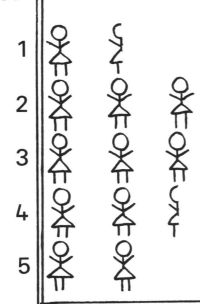

Class

1
2
3
4
5

Number of girls

School meal preference

Girls

Boys

Fish and chips   Salad   Sausage and mash

Key 🍴🍽️ 10 meals

Pictograms

Favourite cartoon characters

Key ☆ 2 people

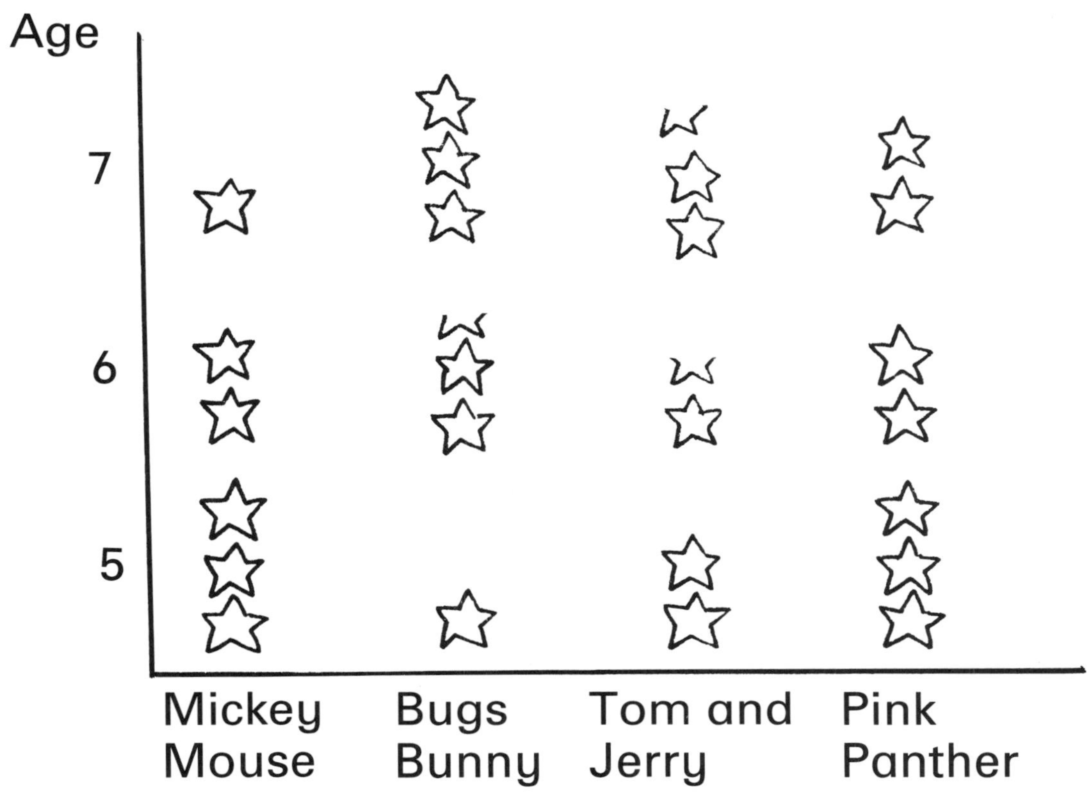

Age

Mickey Mouse | Bugs Bunny | Tom and Jerry | Pink Panther

Does it rain more often on Mondays?

Key ☁ 2 days

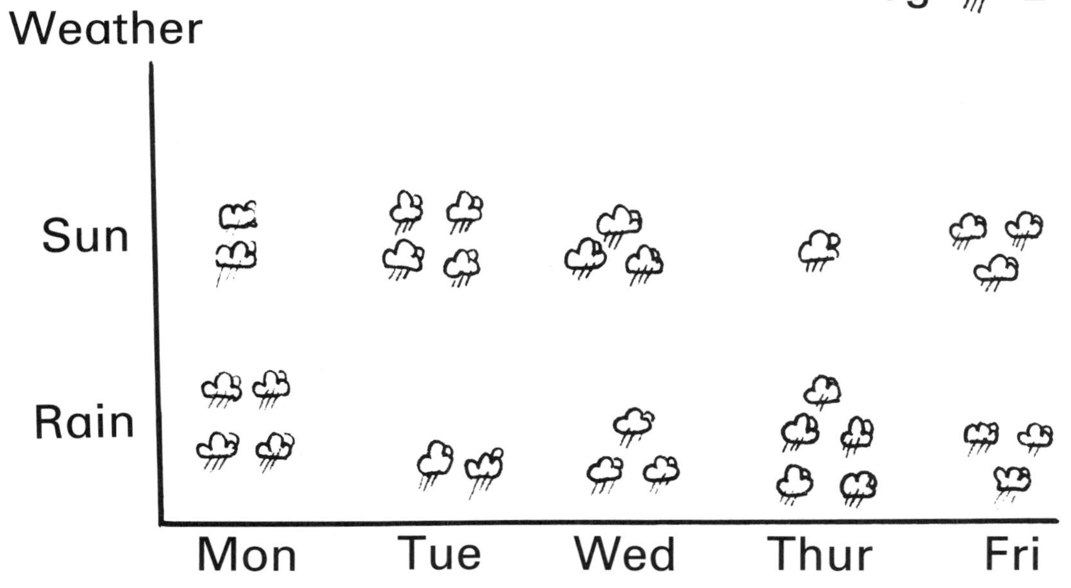

Weather

Mon | Tue | Wed | Thur | Fri

Shape pictures

Draw a man of ○ and ☐

Draw a kite of △

Draw a dog of 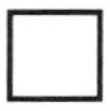 ☐ and △

Draw a house of 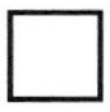 ☐ and ☐

Name _____

Shape match

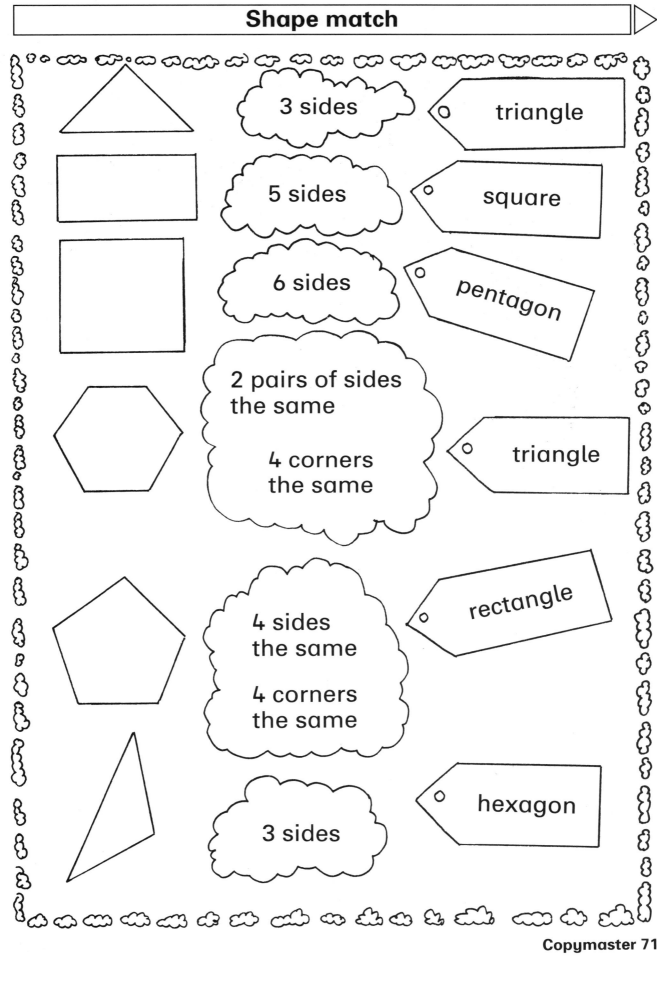

3 sides

5 sides

6 sides

2 pairs of sides the same

4 corners the same

4 sides the same

4 corners the same

3 sides

triangle

square

pentagon

triangle

rectangle

hexagon

Shape match – board

corners all same	4 corners	sides all same	4 sides	square	
corners all same	4 corners	pairs of sides same	4 sides	rectangle	
			6 sides	hexagon	
			5 sides	pentagon	
			3 sides	triangle	

Name _____

Shape match – cards

corners all same	4 corners	sides all same	4 sides	square	
corners all same	4 corners	pairs of sides same	4 sides	rectangle	
			6 sides	hexagon	
			5 sides	pentagon	
			3 sides	triangle	

Cubes and cuboids

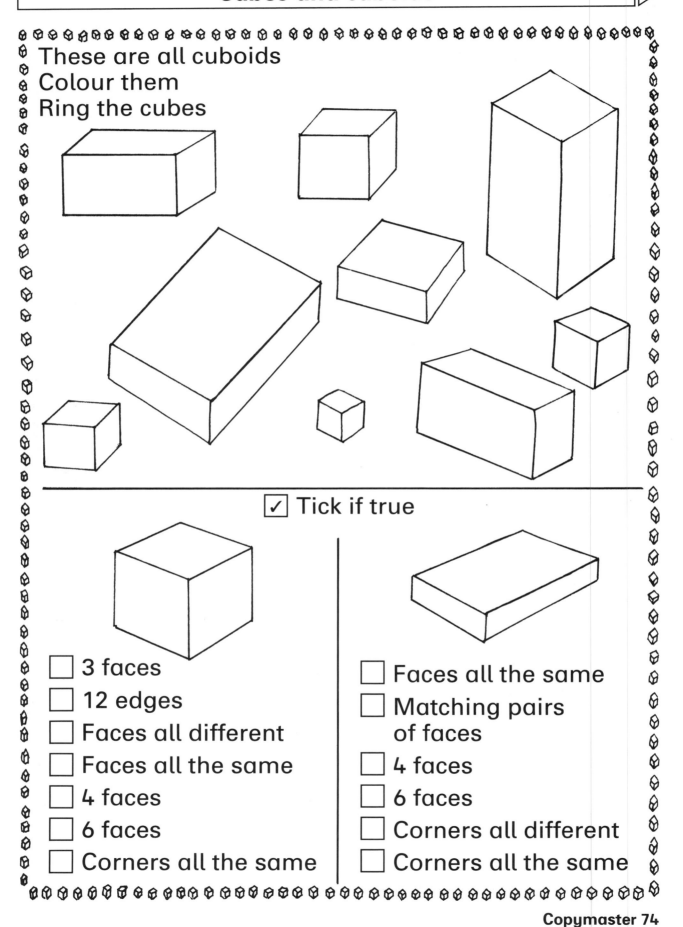

These are all cuboids
Colour them
Ring the cubes

☑ Tick if true

☐ 3 faces
☐ 12 edges
☐ Faces all different
☐ Faces all the same
☐ 4 faces
☐ 6 faces
☐ Corners all the same

☐ Faces all the same
☐ Matching pairs of faces
☐ 4 faces
☐ 6 faces
☐ Corners all different
☐ Corners all the same

Name _____

Cylinders

Draw a cylinder

Draw a cylinder cut open and laid flat

Colour the cylinders

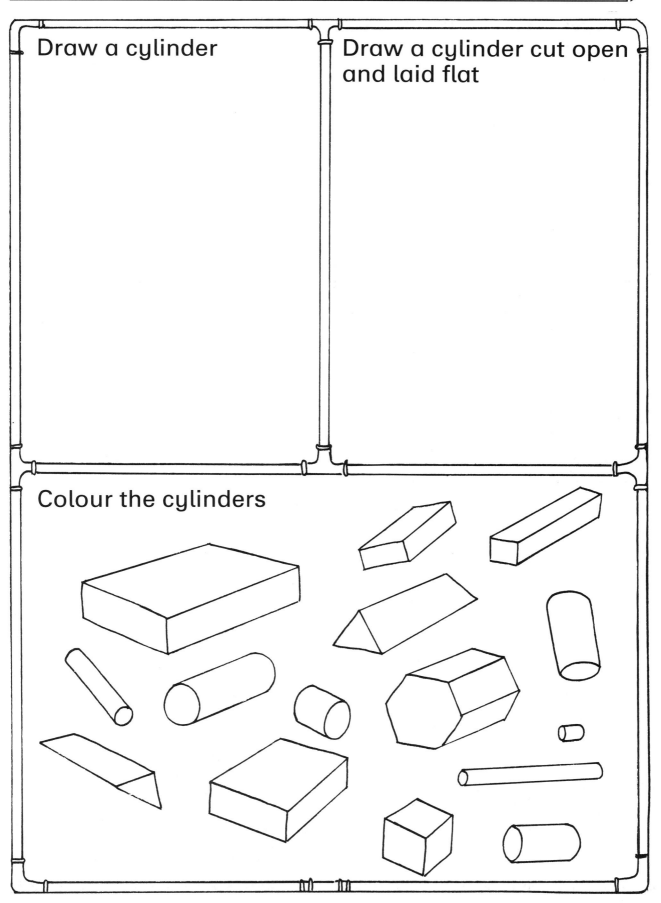

Name _____

3-D shape game – base boards

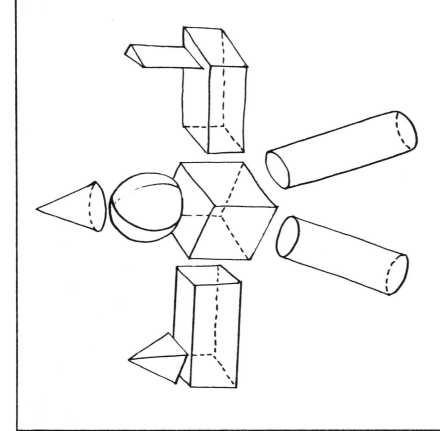

Collect 9 shape cards
to make this model

cuboid – 2   cube – 1
sphere – 1   cylinder – 2
triangular prism – 1
cone – 1   pyramid – 1

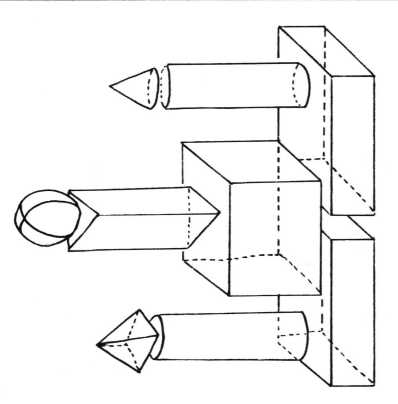

Collect 9 shape cards
to make this model

cuboid – 2   cube – 1
sphere – 1   cylinder – 2
triangular prism – 1
cone – 1   pyramid – 1

Copymaster 76

3-D shape game – base boards

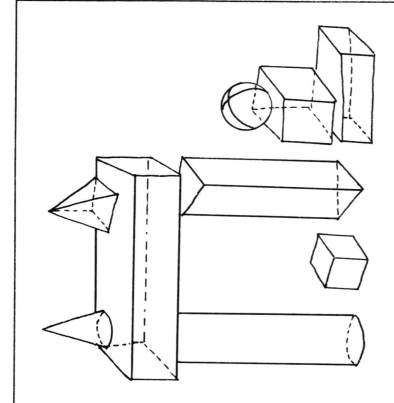

Collect 9 shape cards
to make this model

cuboid – 2   cube – 2
sphere – 1   cylinder – 1
triangular prism – 1
cone – 1   pyramid – 1

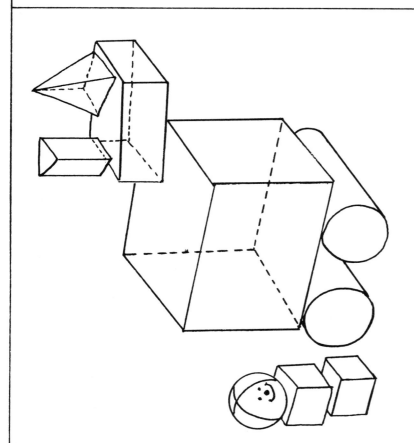

Collect 9 shape cards
to make this model

cuboid – 2   cube – 2
sphere – 1   cylinder – 2
triangular prism – 1
pyramid – 1

3-D shape game – cards

Name _____

2-D shapes quiz

Do you know about shapes?

What can you say about a triangle?

_____

_____

Name the shape with 6 sides _____

What shape has 4 sides the same and
4 corners the same? _____

Name this shape _____

What shape has 5 sides? _____

Name this shape _____

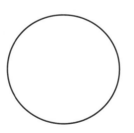

These words
will help you

circle   rectangle   hexagon   pentagon   square

3-D shapes quiz

A die is a _____

A ball is a _____

Telescopes are shaped
like _____

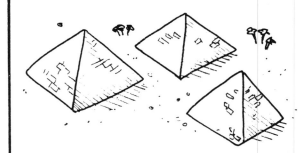

The Egyptians built
the _____

This shape is a
_____

This shape is a
_____

This shape is a
_____

This shape is a _____

cuboid   cube   triangular prism   cone   sphere   hexagonal prism
pyramid   cylinder

Name _____

2-D shapes and symmetry

Colour the symmetrical shapes

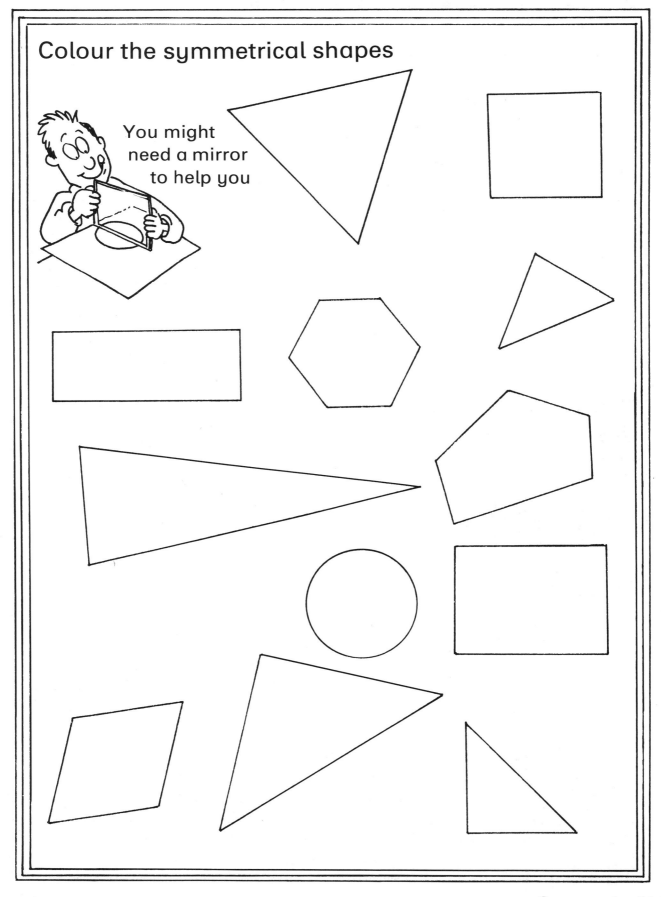

You might
need a mirror
to help you

House number symmetry

7 6 5 4 3 2 1 2 3 4 5 6 7 8 9 0 9 8 7 6 5 4 3 2 1 2 3 4 5

The number on _____ house is _____

Draw the number again.
Make the number so big
it nearly fills the page!

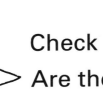

Check the numerals

Are they symmetrical?

3 2 1 2 3 4 5 6 7 8 9 0 9 8 7 6 5 4 3 2 1 2 3 4 5 6 7 8 9 0

Letter symmetry

My name is _____

Draw your name, making the letters large
Tick the letters that are symmetrical

Name _____

Planes of symmetry

Write in how many planes of symmetry each shape has

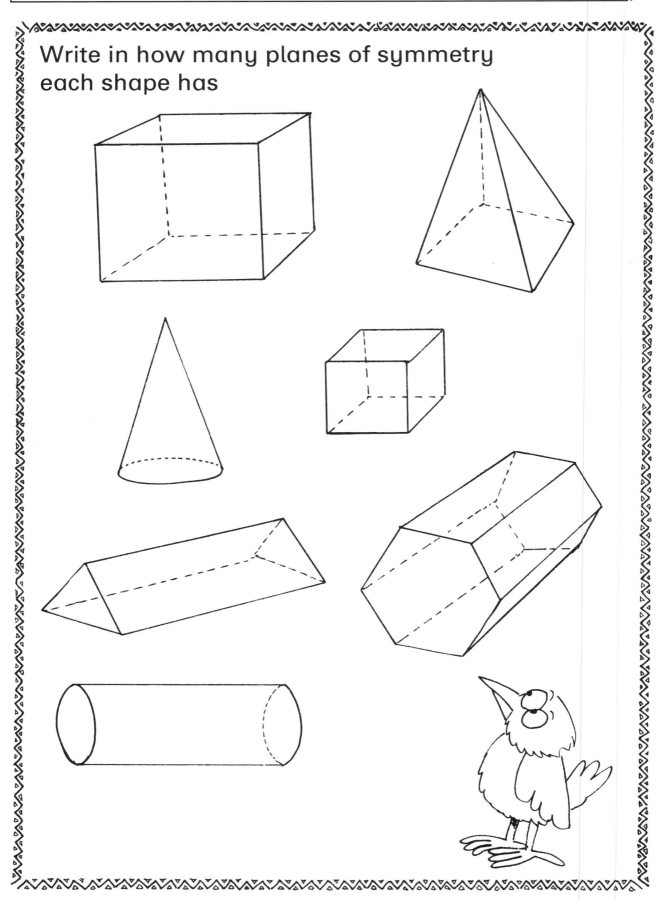

Name _____

Position words

Ring the correct words

under / on

over / down

under / up

down / above

beside / above

on / under

beside / on

up / in front of

behind / over

on / down

above / under

Name _____

Right angles

Draw the things you see with right angles

Mark the right angles

How many can you find?

Name _____

Shapes with right angles

Circle the right angles

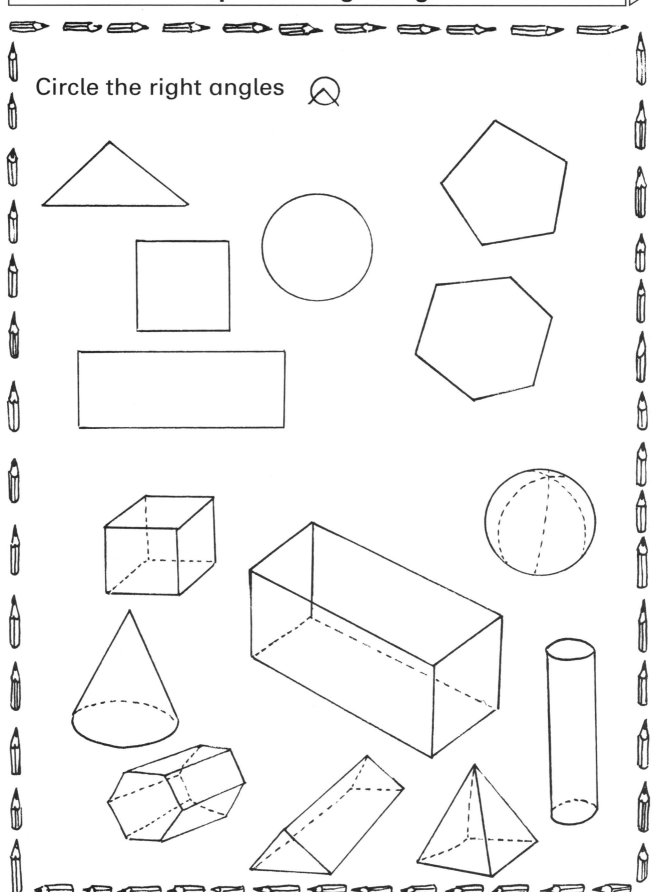

Name _____

Angles around school

Look for angles like these	Where are they? Draw or write
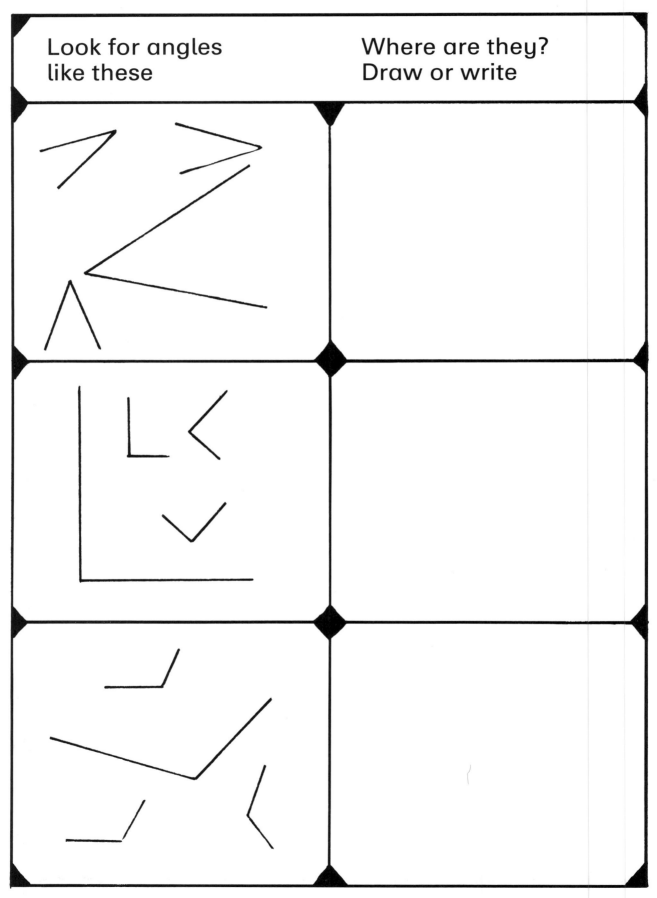	

Shape characters and play titles

Mr Cube   Mrs Cuboid   Little Triangle   Little Square   Little Rectangle

Make up your own characters

What can you call your play?

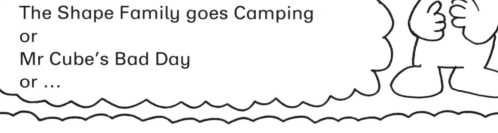

The Shape Family goes Camping
or
Mr Cube's Bad Day
or …

Draw your shape family here

Name _____

Measuring vocabulary

Ring these

2 4 6

Highest number

Smallest drum

Youngest child

Biggest door

Lightest

Fattest fish

Comparing measurements

Draw yourself and two friends

| Me | My friend | My friend |

_____   _____   _____

Draw and write.

Hand _____ has the biggest hand.

Coat _____ has the biggest coat.

Pet/Toy _____ has the smallest pet/toy.

Restaurant comments

Draw what you ate and drank

Write about the food

Name _____

Exciting things to measure with

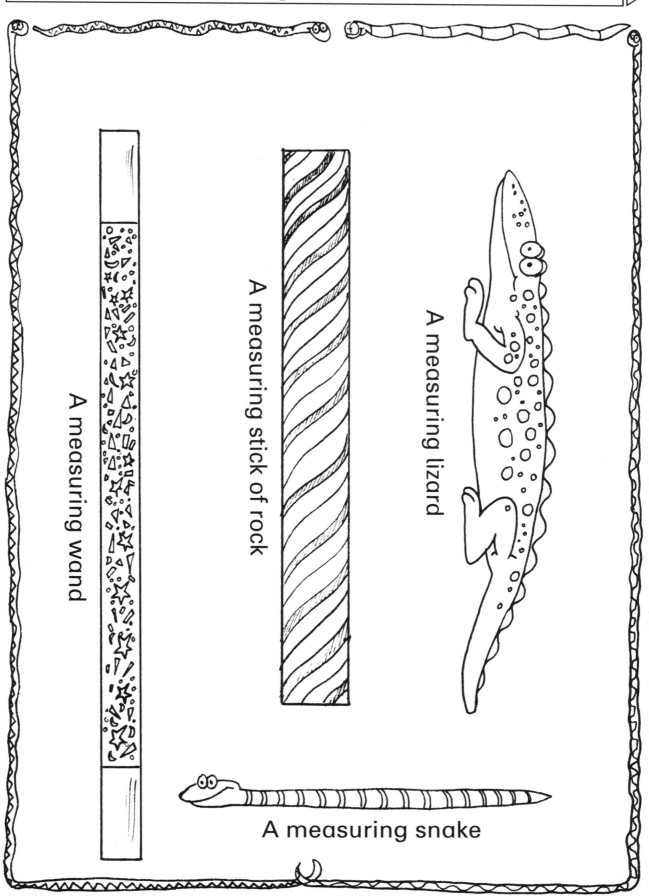

A measuring wand

A measuring stick of rock

A measuring lizard

A measuring snake

Name _____

Measuring: non-standard units

Draw what you measure	Measure with:	How many?
	handspans	
	strides	
	thumbs	
	books	
	pencils	

Capacity

Get four containers of different sizes

Label them

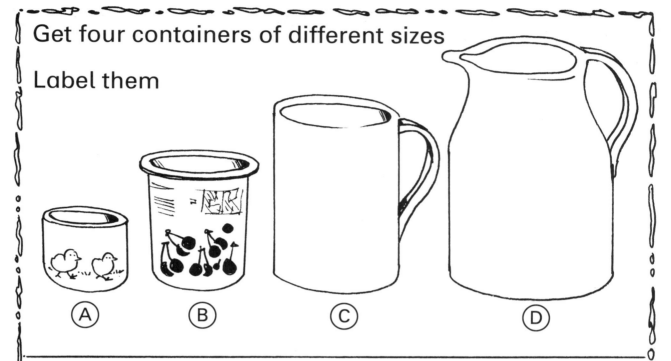

How many?

⬜ Ⓐ fill 1 Ⓑ   ⬜ Ⓑ fill 1 Ⓒ

⬜ Ⓐ fill 1 Ⓒ   ⬜ Ⓑ fill 1 Ⓓ

⬜ Ⓐ fill 1 Ⓓ   ⬜ Ⓒ fill 1 Ⓓ

Do some more using another container

Measuring in centimetres

Measure in centimetres

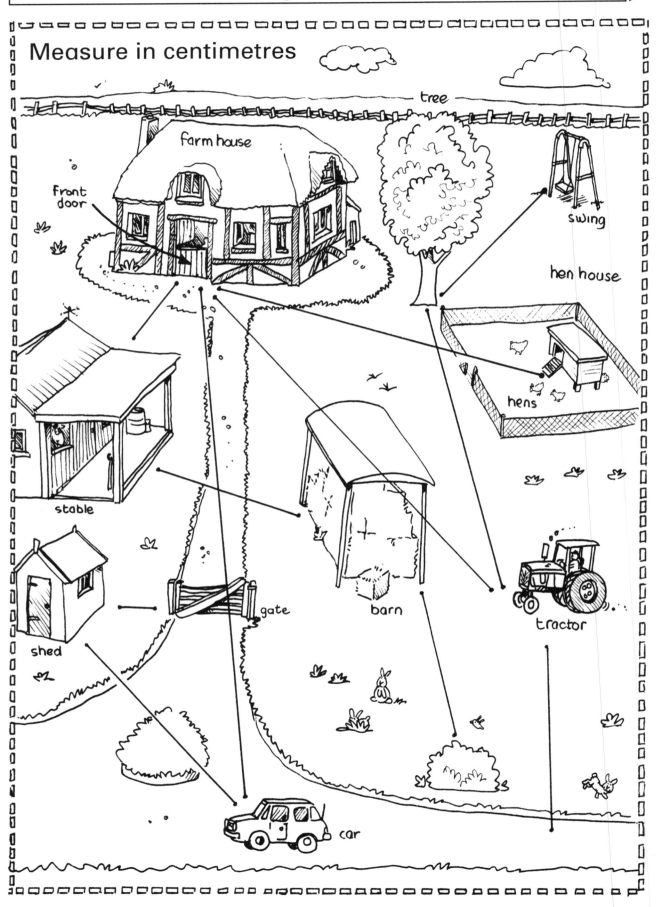

tree

farm house

Front door

swing

hen house

hens

stable

shed

gate

barn

tractor

car

Litres and millilitres

There are _____ millilitres in a litre.

A cup full of tea has _____ ml.

A milk bottle holds _____ ml.

Find some more containers.
Draw them and write on the drawings
what they hold.

Name _____

Clock face

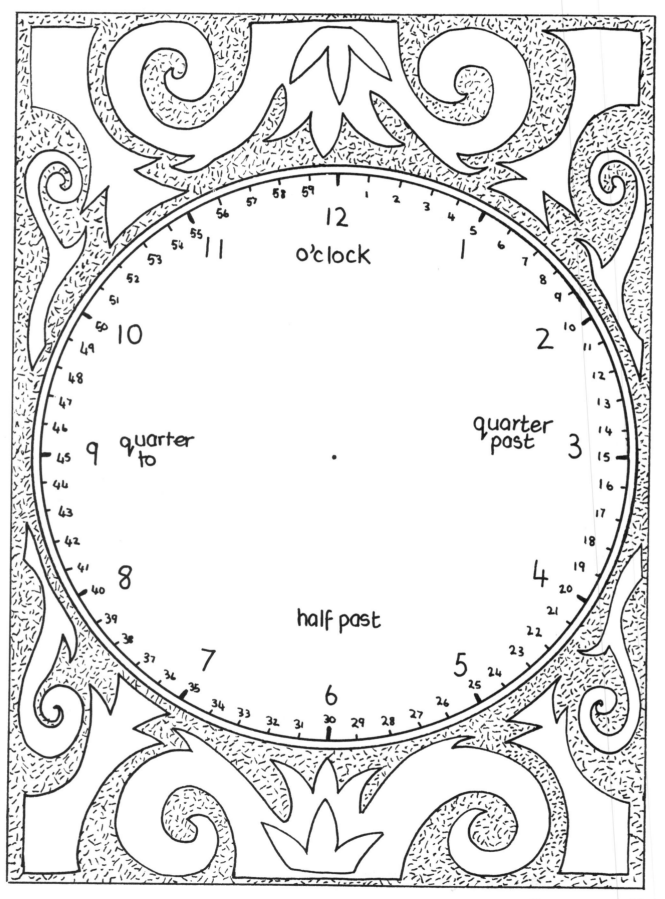

Name _____

Telling the time

What is the time?

The long hand has fallen off these clocks.
Can you still tell the time?

What time will these clocks show 1 hour later?

Digital/written time

Turn these into digital times

four o'clock

half past two

quarter past ten

quarter to one

Write these times in words

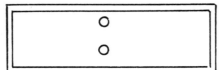

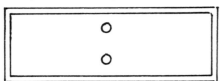

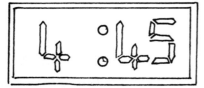

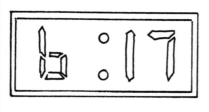

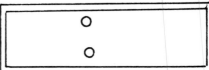

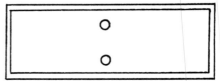

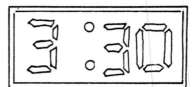

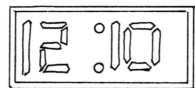

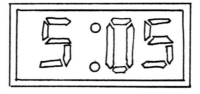

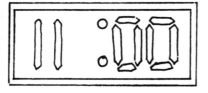

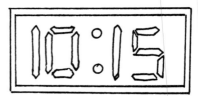

Name _____

Time

Put in the hands

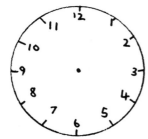 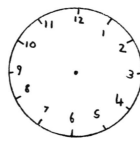 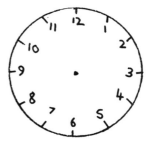

5 o'clock   12 o'clock   9 o'clock

Write in the time

_____   _____   _____

What is the difference in time between these clocks?

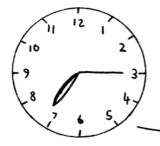 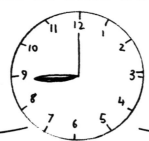 

_____   _____

The long hand has fallen off. What is the time?

_____   _____   _____

Name _____

Spinners

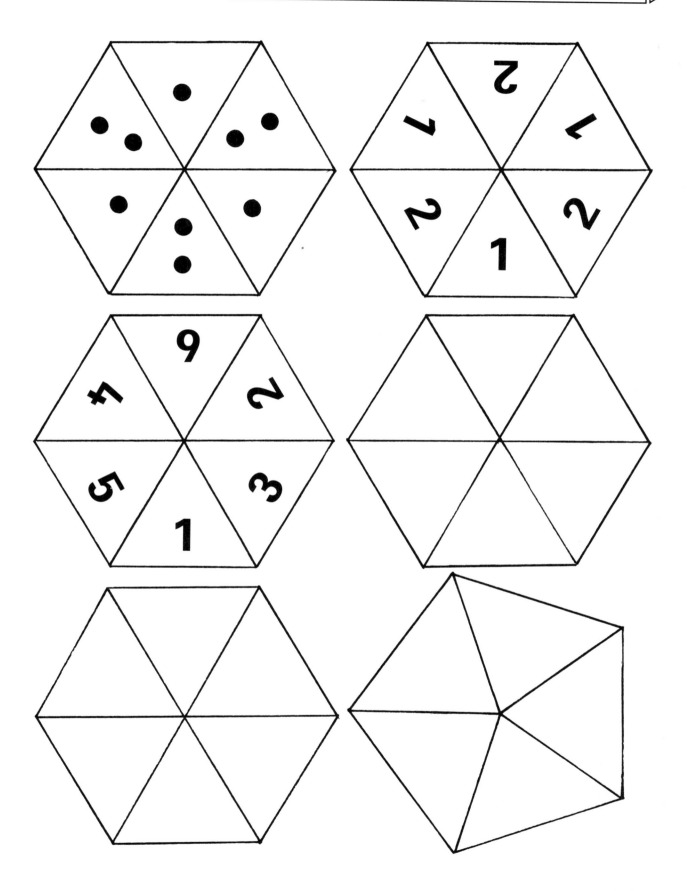

Name _____

Hundred squares

1	2	3	4	5	6	7	8	9	10
11	12	13	14	15	16	17	18	19	20
21	22	23	24	25	26	27	28	29	30
31	32	33	34	35	36	37	38	39	40
41	42	43	44	45	46	47	48	49	50
51	52	53	54	55	56	57	58	59	60
61	62	63	64	65	66	67	68	69	70
71	72	73	74	75	76	77	78	79	80
81	82	83	84	85	86	87	88	89	90
91	92	93	94	95	96	97	98	99	100

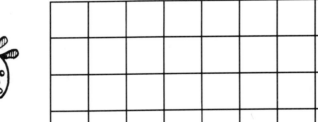
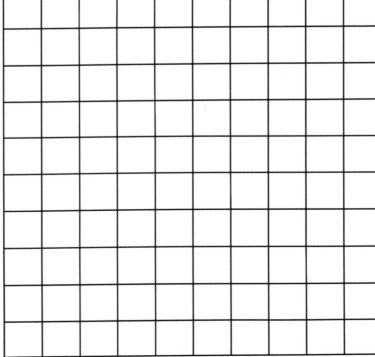

Large hundred square

1	2	3	4	5	6	7	8	9	10
11	12	13	14	15	16	17	18	19	20
21	22	23	24	25	26	27	28	29	30
31	32	33	34	35	36	37	38	39	40
41	42	43	44	45	46	47	48	49	50
51	52	53	54	55	56	57	58	59	60
61	62	63	64	65	66	67	68	69	70
71	72	73	74	75	76	77	78	79	80
81	82	83	84	85	86	87	88	89	90
91	92	93	94	95	96	97	98	99	100

Name _____

Large squares

Name _____

Small squares

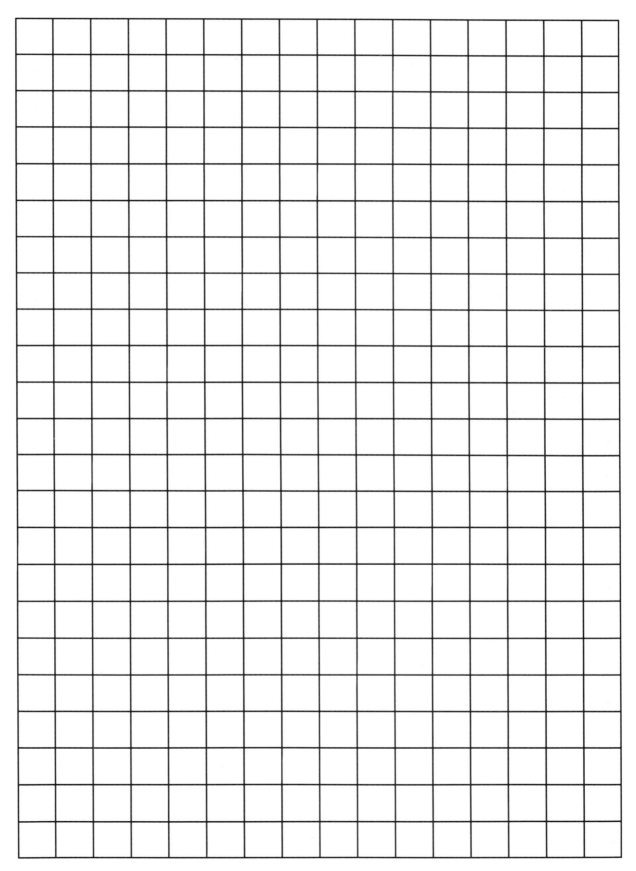

Dotty squares

Name _____

Dotty triangles

Venn diagram: two discrete sets

Draw or list your sets here

Venn diagram: four discrete sets

Venn diagram: two overlapping sets

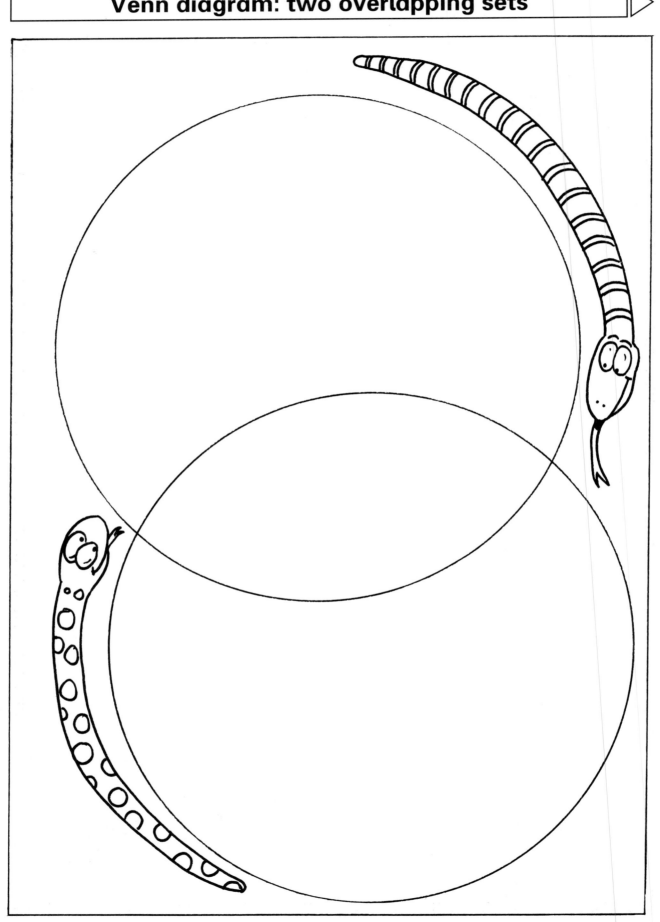

Name _____

Carroll diagram

Record Sheet

Pupil's name _____

AT2 Number	1	2	3	4
	5	6	7	8
	9	10	11	12
	13	14	15	16
	17	18	19	20
	21	22	23	24
	25	26	27	28
	29	30	31	32
	33	34	35	36
	37	38	39	40
	41	42	43	44
	45	46	47	48
	49	50	51	52
	53	54	55	56
	57	58	59	60
	61	62	63	64
	65	66	67	68
	69			
AT3 Shape, Space and Measures	70	71	72	73
	74	75	76	77
	78	79	80	81
	82	83	84	85
	86	87	88	89
	90	91	92	93
	94	95	96	97
	98	99	100	101